Beauty and Hair Fashions
by Suzanne

Drawings by J. Ronald Dahlmann

POPULAR LIBRARY · NEW YORK

CONTENTS

INTRODUCTION

START AT THE TOP

How beautiful is your hair? Is it expertly cut? Radiantly colored? Professionally styled? Or are you faced with the frizzies, fly-away wisps, or a less-than-perfect hairdo?

On the pages that follow, you will find hundreds of helpful hints on oily hair, dry scalp, split ends, fine hair, dandruff, tints, bleaches, shampoos, conditioners, perms, straighteners, plus 55 of the newest coiffure creations from the world's leading hair designers, complete with setting patterns.

In addition, your Tip-Top beauty guide contains the latest, up-to-the-minute information on contouring with makeup, emphasizing your eyes, correcting facial faults, caring for your skin, the do's and don't's of diet, gaining weight, losing weight, exercises, manicures, pedicures . . . and lots more.

Start at the top . . . but don't stop there! Tip-Top shows you the way to total beauty.

CHAPTER I

ALL ABOUT HAIR CARE

Normal Hair . . . Dry Hair . . . Oily Hair . . .
Fine Hair . . . Coarse Hair . . . Thinning Hair
. . . Porous Hair . . . Curly Hair . . . Straighteners . . . Dandruff . . . Haircuts . . . Split Ends
. . . Summer Hair Care . . . Conditioners . . .
Massaging . . . Brushing . . . Hairsprays . . . Shampooing . . . Hair Coloring . . . Perms . . . Plus 25
Hints on Hairpieces and Wigs

ALL ABOUT HAIR CARE

Beautiful hair depends upon a well-balanced diet and constant care. Your hair must be nourished from the inside before it can shine on the outside. If your general health is poor, your hair will certainly show it. Therefore, the first step to hair beauty is a healthy diet. Be sure to get plenty of green, leafy vegetables, fruits, butter, milk, meat, enriched breads, and all the proteins, vitamins, and minerals you need to enhance your crowning glory.

The second step to beautiful hair is constant care. You must know your hair type and how to treat it. Is it dry? Oily? Fine? Coarse? Curly? Porous? Tinted? Bleached? In addition, you must know how to correct such problems as split ends, thinning hair, and dandruff, and know all about brushing, massaging, shampooing, hair coloring, conditioners, hairsprays, perms, haircuts, and daily hair care.

On the pages that follow, you'll find your complete guide to hair care, plus 25 hints on hairpieces and wigs.

WHAT'S YOUR HAIR TYPE?

Normal Hair

Normal hair is shiny, smooth, and easy to manage. It is neither too dry nor too oily. In addition, it is free from dandruff and split ends.

If you're one of the lucky ones who has normal hair . . . don't take it for granted. You, too, need regular hair care.

Shampoo your hair at least once a week, using a shampoo formulated for your hair type. In addition, be sure to keep up daily brushing and massaging so that the natural oils are evenly distributed. To shampoo your hair, lather twice. The first lathering is done with lukewarm water, and finished off with a cream rinse. The cream rinse will make your hair more manageable. A monthly conditioning treatment also helps. In addition, protect your hair from overexposure to sun, wind, and water by wearing protective head coverings.

Dry Hair

Dry hair is dull, brittle, and lackluster. It is usually accompanied by a dry scalp and, very often, by dandruff. Dry hair can be the result of an inadequate diet, overexposure to the sun, or excessive overbleaching. If your hair is dry, learn how to pamper it. Shampoo your hair at least once a week with a special shampoo formulated for your hair type. Brush your hair daily, and don't forget to massage regularly.

Conditioners are a must for dry hair. You can condition your hair with every shampoo. An instant conditioner applied after your shampoo, and a cream rinse following your shampoo, will add shine and luster. In addition, hot oil treatments should be given as often as possible. Start the hot oil treatment about half an hour before your shampoo. Massage warm olive oil into your hair with cotton pads. Cover your hair with a heating cap, or sit under a warm dryer for about fifteen minutes. If you don't have a dryer, wrap your hair for fifteen minutes with a Turkish towel wrung out repeatedly in hot water.

Oily Hair

Oily hair separates easily and has a greasy appearance. It becomes stringy in a few days and often has frizzy ends. Oily hair is the result of overactive oil glands. As a result, if your diet includes fatty foods, it can aggravate the condition.

To take care of oily hair, you must shampoo often. Choose a shampoo especially formulated for your hair type. Three latherings will give you good results. The first two latherings are done in the usual way. However, for the third lathering, leave the shampoo on the hair for fifteen minutes. Then rinse your hair thoroughly. After the shampoo, rinse with a mixture of vinegar and water. Mix one tablespoon of vinegar with a cup of cool water.

Daily brushing is also important for oily hair. This helps distribute the natural oils so they do not accumulate on the scalp. In brushing, cover the brush with cheesecloth to pick up excess oils. In addition, use a cotton pad with witch hazel to remove excess oils between shampoos.

Fine Hair

Fine, limp hair is soft to the touch and doesn't have much body. It doesn't hold a set very well and has a tendency to wilt with humidity. A good perm can add body, and a blunt cut, rather than a layer cut, helps. Fine, limp hair is very often dry and must be treated accordingly. Brushing is especially important, and a daily massage will help stimulate circulation. Avoid too much teasing, and use a soft bristle brush for daily hair care.

Coarse Hair

If your hair is unruly and has a mind of its own, chances are it's coarse and wiry. This type of hair is hard to manage and very resistant. It is difficult to control and has a lot of static electricity. An expert haircut is of great importance, for it makes coarse, wiry hair easier to manage; the hair should be cut in the direction of its natural growth. Try some of the new setting lotions for coarse hair, and use a special spray for hard-to-hold hair.

Thinning Hair

The normal rate of hair loss is about 85 hairs a day. However, if your hair is falling out excessively, see a dermatologist.

For mild cases of dandruff, regular massaging helps considerably. Massage your scalp for about fifteen minutes each day. Use a rotary or circular motion in massaging the scalp. Start at the back, working your way forward. For a dry scalp, apply a little oil before massaging. Generally speaking, avoid teasing of any kind, and be extra gentle in shampooing your hair. Pamper yourself with regular hot-oil treatments, and if you wear a tightly pulled back hairdo, switch to a softer, freer style. In addition, a gentle perm or the use of a wiglet can create extra fullness. Keep your style on either the short or medium side; rather than long.

Porous Hair

If your hair dries quickly after washing or gets tangled and matted when wet, chances are it is porous. Porous hair requires special attention when it comes to coloring or perming. Be sure to give yourself frequent strand tests for best results. Very often, this porous condition is caused by overbleaching and can be corrected with the use of fillers. This type of hair is very sensitive and fragile. When wet, be sure to handle it gently, as it has a tendency to break easily. In addition, stay away from hot dryers, and use a cream rinse after your shampoo.

Curly Hair

Curly hair has a tendency to frizz up when wet, ranging in degree from slightly wavy to kinky. Curly hair usually requires thinning and should be kept all one length, tapering only at the ends. A special setting lotion, as well as jumbo rollers, will create smooth sets. The hairspray you use should also be formulated to your hair type. A hairspray that is too wet will cause the curls to return. For longer-lasting results, get your hair straightened.

Straighteners

For longer-lasting results and a smoother set, curly hair should be straightened on a regular basis. However, don't attempt hair straightening unless your hair is in tip-top condition. If your hair is dry, over-bleached, or damaged, stay away from straighteners until this condition improves. Hair straightening is actually a perm in reverse. You can get your hair straightened once a year, twice a year, or three times a year, depending upon the rate of growth.

If you straighten your hair, be sure to condition it regularly. Condition your hair at least twice a month, or with every shampoo. Never handle your hair roughly, especially when wet, since your hair is extra delicate. When using a dryer, select a low, comfortable temperature, and stay away from curling irons.

Dandruff

A slight show of dandruff is considered normal. Everyone sheds dead skin particles to some degree. However, excessive dandruff can really be a problem for some people. Dandruff can be caused by poor eating habits, vitamin deficiencies, emotional upsets, fatigue, and various other causes. To control this condition, shampoo your hair twice a week with a special medicated or antidandruff shampoo. As you shampoo, be sure to massage your scalp thoroughly so that you remove all the dead flakes of skin. After lathering up, leave the shampoo on your hair for about five minutes. Then rinse it off thoroughly. Finish off with an antidandruff rinse. Stay away from tight-fitting hats, and never borrow anyone else's brush or comb. Brush your hair with a good stiff brush daily, and try to get plenty of sunshine. For acute cases of dandruff, see your dermatologist.

Haircuts

A good haircut is the basis of any hairdo. Without an expert cut, your hair will not hold its line. Select a good hair stylist to do the job. This should not be a do-it-yourself project. Your hair stylist will probably choose between a blunt cut and a taper cut, depending upon your hair type.

A blunt cut is a haircut in which all the hair is the same length. A blunt cut is especially beneficial to fine, limp hair. A taper cut is a haircut in which no two hairs are the same length. For a taper cut, the basic outline is done with a pair of scissors. However, a razor is used to taper each strand. The taper cut is particularly good for coarse hair.

When you go for your haircut, ask your stylist for some professional pointers on caring for your hair between salon visits. Get your hair trimmed often for a well-groomed look, and to remove any split ends.

Split Ends

Split ends give a dry, parched look and a frizzy appearance. They can be caused by incorrect brushing, rough handling, using the wrong type of rollers, etc. To correct this problem, set up a regular conditioning program. Condition your hair before or after every shampoo, and try one of those warm olive oil treatments at home. In setting your hair, use end papers, for they will prevent split ends. Massage the ends with pomade daily.

Summer Hair Care

Extra care is required for your hair during the summer months. The sun, wind, and water have a tendency to dry it out, and you will have to take some protective measures. Keep your hair covered when out in the sun, and always wear a bathing cap while swimming. Chlorine and harsh sun rays can do considerable damage to your hair. Condition your hair regularly. Try one of the conditioners that stays on your hair for about twenty minutes . . . or give yourself a warm olive oil treatment at home. Apply an instant conditioner with every shampoo.

Conditioners

Conditioners add luster and shine to dull, dry hair. Hair that is damaged, bleached, or exposed to sun, wind, or water should be conditioned regularly. Even normal hair benefits from regular treatments. Conditioners can be used before and after every shampoo. In addition, there are shampoos and coloring agents with built-in conditioners to enhance your natural luster. Warm olive oil treatments, which make use of a heating cap, a warm dryer, or Turkish towels wrung out in hot water penetrate deeply into the hair. Protein conditioners are also beneficial and can be used with every shampoo. In addition, apply a hairdressing or pomade to the ends daily, to prevent brittleness.

Massaging

To keep your scalp in tip-top condition, massage daily, before your daily brushing. This stimulates the oil glands and increases circulation. It takes only a few minutes, and the results are well worth it. To massage, place hands at the back of the head, and rotate gently. Use circular motions across the sides and front until the entire scalp is massaged. In shampooing, try one of those plastic or rubber massage brushes to shed loose particles.

Brushing

Brushing stimulates circulation and cleanses your hair and scalp. Natural bristle brushes are best for those daily 100 strokes, whereas nylon brushes are important styling aids. To brush your hair, bend from the waist down, using long, slow strokes. Start at the scalp and work your way down to the very tips. Be careful not to flick the brush roughly as you go along. Brush your hair at least 100 strokes daily, and always brush before your shampoo. In doing the brush-out after a setting, brush your hair out in the opposite direction in which it will be styled. Backbrush for extra height, using a small teasing brush.

Setting Lotion

After washing and rinsing, hair should be towel-dried. It should be damp (not wet) so that your setting lotion will blend nicely. Dribble it on generously through the nozzle of your squeeze bottle. Then simply comb it through hair with a wide-toothed comb. Rayette has two types of hair-setting lotion. Aqua Set in a pale green color is made with a professional gel formula. This is for normal hair. But if you have hard-to-hold hair, the pink Aqua Set is for you. It has a super-hold gel formula that does wonders.

When the gel has been thoroughly combed through hair, it's time for the excitement of setting to start. In the next chapter, you'll read about all the rollers, pin curlers, brushes and combs, all that you'll need. Figure out your setting pattern and go ahead. Should hair seem a bit dry toward the end of setting, just squeeze on a few extra drops of gel.

Hairsprays

A light mist of hairspray is the finishing touch to any new coif. Be sure to choose the right spray for your particular hair needs. Read all the information printed on the can, noting whether or not the spray is water-soluble. Water-soluble means that no shellac, resins, or sticky oils are in the hairspray formula. Water-soluble sprays are easy to wash out, and a wilting set can be revived with the flick of a wet comb. There are a variety of different hairsprays on the market today, namely, sprays for easy-to-hold hair, hard-to-hold hair, color-treated hair, etc.

Rayette's Aqua Net is a professional spray designed to take care of a variety of hair-holding duties. There are three types which are easily identifiable because of the color of their cans. Each is water-soluble, won't affect hair color, and each is an all-weather spray (the dampest weather will not affect its holding power).

The red can is for regular, easy-to-hold hair. So is the blue can—but it is unscented. This is a particular advantage for the woman who does not wish the aura of her perfume to conflict with another scent. Aside from the Aqua Net trio, there are three other sprays which do specific jobs. Aqua Laq, for example, is used for elaborate and extreme hairdos. It will keep the hold in the worst weather conditions. It contains lacquer and is good for active-minded sportswomen. Young Set is for the younger, softer look. It adds bounce and body, and has a firm, soft hold.

For color-treated hair, there is Rayette's Mello Mist which does not strip the color and adds luster to tinted, bleached, or blond hair.

Shampooing

Generally speaking, you should shampoo your hair once a week for normal hair or dry hair, and at least twice a week, or more often, for oily hair. Be sure to select the proper shampoo for your hair type. There are a variety of different shampoos on the market today, namely, shampoos for dry hair, oily hair, normal hair, color-treated hair, etc. In addition, there are special medicated shampoos, antidandruff shampoos, and protein shampoos. If the shampoo is enriched with protein, you can be sure that no film will be left and that there will be no streaks or discoloration. If your hair has been colored, select a noncolor-stripping shampoo. All these built-in features are in Aqua Net Protein Shampoo. This shampoo adds body so that the hair is easier to style. These same advantages are also true of Aqua Net Special Shampoo, which has the added advantage of being great for any woman with even the mildest dandruff condition.

Before shampooing, brush out your hair to remove all the tangles. Massage your scalp, using firm but gentle motions. Wet your hair with warm water and apply the shampoo. Lather well, massaging soapsuds into the scalp. If you have any makeup particles at the front hairline, use a small nailbrush to remove them.

Hair Coloring

There are three basic categories of hair coloring, namely, temporary rinses, semipermanent hair coloring, and permanent hair coloring.

Temporary rinses wash out with each shampoo. They merely coat the hair shaft. Temporary rinses are used to highlight or enhance your natural color. The shades are natural-looking and can be used to tone down unwanted reds and golds, or to add depth to your own hair color.

Semipermanent hair coloring lasts about five times as long as temporary rinses. These hair coloring agents penetrate the outer layer of the hair shaft. Semipermanent colorings are used to brighten, lighten, or cover gray. However, be sure to give yourself a patch test before using. The patch test will indicate whether or not you are allergic to the product.

A tint is a permanent form of hair coloring. Tints that are shampooed into the hair are very popular because they are easy to use and the color is controlled automatically. Tints last until the hair grows out and are available in a large variety of colors. A patch test must be taken prior to applying any tints. You can use a tint to change your hair color several shades, to cover unsightly gray, or to add radiant color. Tints are usually packaged in kits that contain the tint, the developer, and plastic gloves. Be sure to follow the manufacturer's instructions carefully.

Lighteners and bleaches are used to prepare the hair for light, pastel shades. In addition, there are mild blonding kits on the market today, which lighten dark-blondes and brownettes gently. Pre-bleaching is necessary when you want the pale blond or red shades. The bleach is left on the hair until enough pigment is removed, and then a toner is applied to the hair.

Unusual effects such as tipping, streaking, and frosting add glamour and excitement to any hairdo. In frosting, the hair to be bleached is pulled out of a perforated cap with a crochet needle.

If your hair is in bad condition, never color it until

this condition is corrected. In addition, do not tint your eyebrows or eyelashes, as this can cause blindness. Always wear rubber gloves when applying the color, as they will protect your hands from possible irritation.

With a new change of color, remember that you will have to change your cosmetics to match. If you have lightened your hair, be sure to use a lighter foundation and to give your cheeks a glow with a rosy blusher or gel. Hair that has been tinted or bleached will also require more frequent conditioning. Although the new products contain built-in conditioners be sure to condition your hair at least once a month to restore the natural oils.

Perms

Perms are especially beneficial to fine, limp hair. In addition, they are used to provide body and springiness to the current styles. In perming, hair is wrapped around rods and then softened through a chemical process. The neutralizer locks the hair into the new shape.

Three important considerations in any perm are the porosity, the elasticity, and the texture of your hair. Porosity refers to the ability of your hair to absorb moisture. Bleached hair is more porous than virgin hair. Elasticity refers to the springiness of the hair to be permed. If you overwave coarse hair, you will wind up with frizzy ends. In perming, be sure to choose the right kind of wave for your hair type. The size of the rods will give you loose, casual waves, or tight, springy curls.

Generally speaking, before perming, trim the ends of your hair. Be sure to blunt-cut fine hair and taper coarse hair. Take a patch test before each perm, and wait at least two weeks before perming color-treated hair. Perm kits are available for every hair type, and the instructions are easy to follow. However, don't attempt a perm if you have any scalp irritations. Wait until the condition clears up. In addition, after your perm, pamper your hair with frequent conditioning treatments.

A perm lasts until it grows out—which is about two to three months. In doing it at home, you will need a perm kit, cotton pads, end papers, and a timer. Follow the instructions, handling the hair gently while you shampoo.

25 Hints on Hairpieces and Wigs

1. In attaching a fall, be sure to cover the joining with a hair band, or a mini-braid tied at the center. You can even use strands of your own hair, arranging hair in crisscross fashion.

2. To set a human hair wig, use plastic rollers. Dampen each section as you go along, using end papers for a smoother set.

3. Human hair wigs should be conditioned regularly. If you condition the wig after it is cleaned, it will make the hair more manageable.

4. Style a synthetic wig with a wire brush or a special wig brush for best results.

5. Braids are a great way to dress up a hairdo. A single braid can be wrapped around the hair and tied at the forehead, or a bunch of braids can be attached at the side.

6. Never try to tint a synthetic wig. Synthetic wigs do not take to tints. If you're not satisfied with the color, buy a new one rather than experiment with the old one.

7. To attach a fall, make a few pincurls with your own hair, crisscrossing the pins. Insert the small comb, which usually comes with the fall, securely underneath the pins.

8. If your hair is fine and could use some extra volume, attach a wiglet wherever you need it. First think of your hairdo, and then attach the wiglet at the crown or back to create the desired effect.

9. To put on a wig, the first thing to do is to get your own hair out of the way. You can pin it up with pincurls which not only reduces the bulk but also sets your hair at the same time.

10. Brush your wig as you would your own hair. Brushing will remove any roller marks and it will relax the curl. Use a special wig brush with wire bristles.

11. Use a temporary color rinse on a human hair wig to tone down brassy reds and golds.

12. To style your wig, work on a wig block or your own head. If you don't need any teasing, just brush your wig into shape. Attach the wig to your own head. Wet each section as you go along.

13. To find out if a wig needs cleaning, first brush the hairpiece out thoroughly. Remove the hairspray, dirt, and grime which accumulate, and if the wig still feels dirty, clean it.

14. You can change your hair color instantly with a wig. If you've always wanted to be a blonde, and never got around to doing so, become a blonde instantly with a wash 'n' wear stretch wig.

15. A great way to camouflage dark roots that need a retouching is to wear some pin-on bangs, or wear a head band.

16. A switch is one of the most versatile hairpieces. It is a long hank of hair from 20 to 35 inches long, and can be made into a braid, a ponytail, etc.

17. Human hair wigs need setting lotions for firmer sets. The setting lotion should be resistant to dampness, and especially formulated for use on wigs.

18. After setting a wig, dry it immediately in a warm dryer, covering it with a net. Do not let your hairpiece or wig stay wet overnight.

19. Wigs are a must for traveling. Synthetics travel best and can be thrown into your suitcase.

20. Human hair wigs can be treated with a color rinse to restore faded coloring. A temporary color rinse will restore hair to its original color.

21. Wiglets can be used to add body to fine hair, to create the illusion of fullness, and to cover up split ends.

22. To attach a wig, slip it onto your head, using both hands. Check to see if the hairline is even with yours. Insert comb, brushing a few strands of your own hair over the wig at the front hairline.

23. After cleaning a wig, place it on block while damp. Brush hair while damp, making sure that wig block is the same size as wig.

24. To set a wig, use long, rust-free pins to hold rollers in place. Be careful not to jab the foundation with clips or hairpins.

25. To clean a synthetic wig, swish wig through suds. Use a wide-toothed comb to separate strands. Brush wig out thoroughly with a special wig brush.

CHAPTER II

TIP-TOP STYLING SECRETS

Professional Pointers on Rollers, Clip Curls, Brushes, Combs, Stylers, Shapers, Accessories, Sleepers, Cover-Ups, Bows, Barrettes, and Jewelry . . . Plus 50 Professional Styling Secrets

TIP-TOP STYLING SECRETS

Now that you know all about hair care, Tip-Top shows you the way to professional-looking sets and styles. Between salon visits, you can become a do-it-at-home expert by following Tip-Top's 50 Professional Styling Secrets. But before you do, brush up on some of the basics of setting and styling your hair.

THE RIGHT WAY TO USE ROLLERS

Rollers come in a variety of different sizes. You can choose from small, medium, large, medium bouffant, large bouffant, and jumbo bouffant. In addition, there are a variety of stubby sizes. You may need several different-size rollers for your setting, or the same roller size throughout. For long, maxi hairdos, choose the jumbo rollers. Jumbo rollers can also be used to tame down too curly locks, or for extra-smooth sets. Use large rollers on long hair for a slightly firmer finish. Medium-size rollers are for styles that require curls, bounce, waves, or firmness. Small rollers are used to set tendrils along the sides of the face and along the nape-line. Small rollers are perfect for short, curly coifs.

In winding the rollers, hold the hair straight up from the scalp. Each section should be free from any snarls or tangles. Saturate each strand with setting gel and comb through. Use end papers for a smoother set. Never wind rollers too tightly as you can cause hair breakage. Place rollers close together to avoid any separations in the finished style. Use Tip-Top roller pins to hold rollers in place. The roller pins vary in size from jumbo to deluxe, and have easy-grip con-toured heads and nonslip shaft anchors.

DIFFERENT KINDS OF ROLLERS

In addition to selecting the right roller size, be sure to choose the type of roller that best suits your hair. The Tip-Top styling wardrobe includes a variety of different rollers, namely, magnetic rollers, brush rollers, color-coded brush rollers, controllers, foam-cushion rollers, and snap-on rollers.

Magnetic Rollers

Magnetic rollers are smooth and perforated for fast drying. They are ideal for tinted, bleached, or problem hair. Magnetic rollers are color-coded and are wash-able. They come in a variety of different sizes, namely, small, large, jumbo, and four different stubby sizes. In addition, you can choose from medium bouffant, large bouffant, and jumbo bouffant.

Brush Rollers

Brush rollers grip better and dry fast. They have a circular brush in the center that grips the hair. Tip-Top's Featherlight Professional Brush Rollers have smooth, flexible brushes that won't scratch or snag. They are made of aluminum coil, and the braid makes them comfortable and durable. The Deluxe Professional Brush Rollers range in size from small to jumbo bouffant.

Color-Coded Brush Rollers

Color-coded brush rollers are constructed in the same way as regular brush rollers except that they are color-coded with "poly" braid. There are six colors—each indicating a different size. For example, red indicates a large bouffant roller, whereas lavender indicates a small roller.

Controllers

Tip-Top Controllers are brush-type rollers, made of extruded plastic. They are designed for comfort and convenience and for the perfect hairdo. Many women prefer controllers to rollers since they are as soft as foam, curl like a magnetic roller, and hold like a brush roller. Controllers come in a variety of different sizes, namely, large, jumbo, and medium bouffant.

Snap-On Rollers

Snap-on rollers have an hourglass shape with tiny teeth. There is no bunching in the center or loosening at the sides with Tip-Top's exclusive hourglass shape.

The clamp allows hair to dry faster, and it goes on in a jiffy. Plastic snap-on rollers come in a variety of different sizes, ranging from small to medium bouffant.

Foam-Cushion Rollers

Foam-cushion rollers are the softest and most comfortable rollers for sleeping. The foam is fast-drying, and the two-piece flexible core locks the curl from any position and holds it. Foam-cushion rollers come in a variety of different sizes, including small, medium, large, and medium bouffant.

HOW TO MAKE CLIP CURLS

Clip curls require dexterity and skill. Clip curls are used to set tendrils, catch short ends at the nape of the neck, and for all pincurl settings. They should be uniform in size. To make cheek curls, first saturate hair with setting gel and comb through. Wind comma curls toward face, and reverse curls in the opposite direction. Catch ends with end papers for best results. Clip into place.

To make clip curls, first comb each strand through to remove tangles. Hold strand straight down, winding curl around finger at midpoint. Slide clip in, catching ends in prongs. Tip-Top Clipettes can't crimp the curl or snag hair. In addition, there is an E-Z finger grip with firm, smooth action. The full-length ventilating slots shorten drying time, and they are fast and easy to insert or remove. Clip curls can also be used to set ringlets.

Stand-up clip curls are used to set bouncy, short

coifs. To set, comb each strand straight from scalp. Wind strand straight down to scalp, sliding clip in close to base.

MAKING FINGER WAVES

Jumbo clips about 3½ inches in length are perfect for making waves. Finger waves, in particular, are easy to make with Tip-Top Jumbo Clips. To make finger waves, saturate hair with setting gel and comb through. Form waves by molding hair with comb and the side of the hand. Insert king-size clips to hold waves in place. Jumbo clips have a flat, hold-tight spring, and are made of smooth aluminum.

SETTING AND STYLING WITH BOB PINS

In setting your air with bob pins, be sure to use pins with rubber-coated tips. Tip-Top Bob Pins are double-coated baked enamel and have a satin-smooth finish. Teardrop tips of synthetic rubber protect the hair and scalp. They open easily, hold securely, and slide out smoothly. A handy plastic box contains 400 regular-size bob pins.

Jumbo-size bob pins are ideal for holding rollers, hairpieces, and wigs. Tip-Top's Jumbo Size Bob Pins are 2¾ inches long and have soft teardrop ends. Tip-Top Jumbo Hair Pins about 3 inches long can be used for setting and styling. These pins have a permanent finish with metal ball tips.

KINDS OF CURLERS

Soft Vinyl Curlers

In addition to roller and clip curl settings, some women prefer the soft vinyl curlers or aluminum curlers. Tip-Top's Flexible Soft Vinyl Dream Curlers have a one-piece construction with nothing to break or come apart. The flexible vinyl plastic never crimps, and these curlers can be used with any styling solution. They are perforated for quicker drying and are great for women with baby-fine hair. Children find them comfortable, too.

Aluminum Curlers

Aluminum curlers have polished-smooth edges and cannot come apart. The smooth, lightweight aluminum is perforated, and the built-in clamp has a zippy spring. Available in several different sizes, these curlers are great for fast-recovery hairdos. (A handy accessory to keep on hand, regardless of the type of curlers you use, is a catchall with inside tray to hold curlers, rollers, clips, combs, etc.)

Magicurl Curlers

In addition to soft vinyl curlers and aluminum curlers, Tip-Top also has Magicurl Curlers for home perms. The $2\frac{1}{4}$-by-$\frac{5}{16}$ inch rods can be used with any type of wave. The lightweight and flexible plastic body is hollow and perforated. These soft curlers allow complete saturation.

PROFESSIONAL POINTERS
ON BRUSH-OUTS

In doing the brush-out for a particular style, brush the hair out in the opposite direction of the finished style. Brush firmly but vigorously, being careful not to pull the hair. For everyday use, use a natural bristle brush. For teasing and backbrushing, there are special nylon brushes and styling aids to do the trick. For smoothing, lifting, and poufing, a hair lift does wonders. The tip of a rattail comb can be used to create layered effects. Finish the style with a light mist of spray especially formulated for your hair type.

BRUSHES AND COMBS

To become an expert do-it-at-home stylist, you must know all about brushes and combs and how to use them. Tip-Top's styling wardrobe includes brushes for heavy hair, brushes for softer hair, styling brushes, beautician's brushes, wide-tooth combs for wet hair, fine-tooth combs for finishing touches, rattail combs, teasing combs, hair lifts, and just about everything else to enhance your crowning glory.

The Beautician's Brush

The beautician's brush is 7 ¾ inches long, and is both functional and beautiful. It has flared nylon bristles

THE BEAUTICIAN'S BRUSH

and is gentle to the hair and scalp. A palm-curved handle with thumb rest makes it easy to handle. It is made of unbreakable plastic and comes in a variety of different colors.

The Wig and Hairbrush

The wig and hairbrush is especially suitable for long, heavy hair, and it is used for wigs, wiglets, and

THE WIG AND HAIRBRUSH

falls. It never pulls or snags, as the wire bristles, carefully machined and polished, glide through even the thickest hair. A rubber back adds to the cushiony effect, and this type of brush is extremely durable.

The Purse-Size Styling Brush

The purse-size styling brush is 7 inches long and has flared nylon bristles in two lengths for easy back-brushing or teasing. It fits easily into a handbag, and has a palm-curved handle with thumb rest.

Professional Styling Hairbrush

The professional styling hairbrush has a contoured back and handle for complete styling ease. It is made

PROFESSIONAL STYLING HAIRBRUSH

of beautiful satin-finish unbreakable poly. The flared nylon bristles are gentle to the scalp and hair, while being firm and effective. The dresser size is 8 inches long.

The Professional Half-Round Brush

The professional half-round brush with smooth nylon bristles won't scratch the scalp or tear the hair. Palm-contoured handle makes styling and brushing a pleasure. The bristles flare from a half-round base, and the contoured handle makes it easy to use.

The Clubman's Brush

The clubman's hairbrush is great for morning and night brushings. It is good for heavy, coarse hair and helps to remove persistent tangles. It has a contoured handle and head. Its sturdy nylon bristles are contoured to the curve of the head to allow quick and thorough brushing. It is made of unbreakable poly.

The French-Flare Styling Brush

The French-flare styling brush is a long, skinny brush with curved pearl-tone plastic back and handle. It is excellent for styling, and its brisk nylon bristles are contoured to the curve of the head. There is a 9-inch dresser size, and the handle has a thumb hold.

The 9-inch French-flare styling brush with flared nylon bristles, rattail handle, and thumb rest is great for lifting and styling.

Brush-and-Comb Sets

The purse set has a rattail styling comb 6½ inches long with matching 6¼-inch brush of flared poly bristles. It is made of gleaming pearl-tone plastic. The brush 'n' comb vanity set is in elegant pearl-tone plastic and is unbreakable. An all-purpose 7-inch comb matches a 7¼-inch brush. The brush has firm but gentle poly bristles. It is packaged in a clear poly case.

SPECIAL STYLING COMBS

The Professional Hair Lift

The professional hair lift lifts, fluffs, and smooths, giving a professional touch to any hairdo. It is hand-

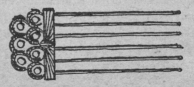

THE PROFESSIONAL HAIR LIFT

finished and so decorative it can be used as an orna-
mental comb for a chignon. It has an openwork design
in Florentine finish, and it is made of rustproof metal.

Aluminum Combs

Nonstatic imported aluminum combs are practical
and handsome. Satin-smooth teeth coupled with nonstatic features assures easy comb-through on any head
of hair. They are rustproof and indestructible, and
come in a vinyl carrying case. Included in the group
of aluminum combs are a rattail styling comb, an all-
purpose dresser comb, a combination hair lift and styling comb, a pocket comb, and a teasing styler with
smooth teeth. The combs are made of satin-finished
aluminum.

The Barber Comb

The 7-inch barber comb has both thick and thin
teeth. It won't scratch the hair or scalp. It has a polished finish and is a basic comb to have on hand.

All-Purpose Combs

All-purpose dresser or purse combs are available in
assorted colors. All-purpose combs are a must for
every styling wardrobe. These combs are contoured to
fit the scalp.

STYLING AIDS

The Professional Hair Styler

The professional hair styler is a comb-brush with three rows of polished teeth. In addition, it has a rat-tail handle, with parting teeth at the end. It is made of unbreakable poly and comes in a variety of colors.

The Mini-Styler

The mini-styler has regular-size teeth on one side and mini teeth on the other. It's great for all kinds of

THE MINI-STYLER

backcombing problems. The rattail handle is ideal for lifting, and there is an easy thumb grip.

The Professional Styling Comb

This all-purpose comb has tiny teeth at one end and wider ones at the other. With just the slightest flick of the finger, an adjustable slide releases a tiny rattail from one end.

The Swirl Styler

The swirl styler has a unique curved form for extra-easy backcombing action. There is a rattail handle which has an exclusive tooth design for gentle teasing. It is made from unbreakable poly.

The 3-in-1 Styler

The 3-in-1 styler is for combing, teasing, and lifting. It is made of guaranteed unbreakable poly and has super-smooth regular and teasing teeth. The 3-in-1 styler has an easy-grip handle.

The Comb-Brush

The comb-brush looks like a brush, but acts like a comb. The three rows of teeth are as sturdy as in any comb, but this styling accessory can give the vigorous treatment of a strong brush. The comb-brush has three rows of polished teeth and a contoured rattail handle.

The Hair Trimmer and Shaper

The hair trimmer and shaper is a handy instrument for trimming between visits. The hair trimmer and shaper with a 5-inch ruler on the handle, double-edge blade, and complete instructions on the back of the card, is easy to use. It is 7¼ inches long and has a tapered handle. The 5-inch ruler on the handle makes measuring easy while snipping. In addition, the styling skill/trimming set includes a rattail styling comb with nonscratch teeth.

ENHANCE YOUR HAIRDO WITH
HAIR ACCESSORIES

Use your imagination to enhance your hairdo with bandeaux, hair bands, barrettes, and bows. In addition, evening hair jewelry ranging from jeweled clips to coiffure bands add fashion excitement.

Bandeaux

Bandeaux are hair controllers ranging from ¼ inch to 1 inch in width. They come in a variety of colors and include velvet-covered plastic bandeaux with tailored bows, high-fashion tiara-styled coiffure bands, and casual medium to wide plastic bandeaux. Tip-top bandeaux are smoothly contoured of highly polished plastic with double rows of gripping teeth.

Use a hair band to dress up your coiffure or to add a note of gaiety. By using a hair band, you can control your hair and at the same time reveal a smooth, uncluttered hairline. Leather hair bands can be worn around the forehead in contemporary style. Leather hair bands come in black, brown, and tan leather, and have multicolor wooden beads and leather thong ties. Knit hair bands are comfortable to wear, and include flat knits, rib knits, nubby-looking and crocheted nylons, bulky knits, crisscross weave nylons, and novelty bas-relief bands.

Sun 'n' fun bands are ideal for beachwear and swimming. Terry tie-ons in bright assorted prints are great for beach and active sports. In addition, there are smart vinylette bowknot bands and crush-resistant velvet bands with tailored bows.

Bows

Velvet bows on bob pins or curl clips, as well as nylon-velvet bows tied on bob-pins, add sparkle to any hairdo. Mini-bows emphasize your coif, and can be worn scattered throughout your hairdo. Extra-large velvet bows or a large butterfly velvet bow can enhance a cluster of curls or a chignon at the back of the head.

Barrettes and Clasps

Barrettes can be used to hold back a heavy hank of hair or to accent a feminine hairdo. Tip-Top barrettes and clasps are trained to stay put because they have either double wire-back locks or steel spring clasps. Another assurance that they will stay where they belong is that most of them have either a foam spring grip or fine teeth on the back.

Delightful fashion touches to a pretty coif are the barrette and scarf holders. These hair accessories can be used for bows, scarves, or yarn ties. A unique innovation is the snap 'n' match barrette. Any fabric can be snapped into the center portion for a perfect costume match-up. The plastic center snaps out quickly and easily, and the 4-inch golden-finish buckle has a double-wire lock teeth gripper.

Included in the Tip-Top collection are golden Florentine-finish barrettes with double-wire locks, mother-of-pearl plastic barrettes, ornate plastic wood-grain barrettes, and gold mirror overlay barrettes. In addition, there are engraved metal barrettes, fabric barrettes, mock-tortoise clasps with mother-of-pearl plastic, and multicolor flowers on one-piece barrettes. The chignon comb, 5 inches wide in shell plastic, and the ever-popular tortoise barrette, are fashion favorites.

Buckles

Besides barrettes, jumbo sweep buckles of imported shell hold back heavy hanks of hair. Intricate bamboo sweep buckles, authenticated Oriental and leather sweep buckles of pliant leather are both functional and decorative. The miracle vinyl sweep buckle combines the comfort of vinyl foam with the flexibility of leather. The shapes in the collection include ovals, bows, ellipses, swirls, butterflies, and peace symbols. Textures vary from reptile to wet-looking patterns. The tortoise sweep buckle with French clasp holds hair in place. Besides being functional, it is especially rich-looking. The tortoise sweep buckle is great for ponies and pulls.

Ponytail Barrettes and Holders

Ponytail barrettes and holders hold hair securely in place, while decorating it.

PONYTAIL BARRETTE

Handy bands are elastic tail holders, and the all-purpose handy bands are made of heavy-duty rubber. The no-tangle elastic cord pigtail and ponytail holders have gold-finish metal-ball ends. The elastic pigtail and ponytail holders lock the hair firmly and are simple to use. The Tip-Top collection also includes jiffy grip ponytail holders, which are red, blue, and yellow rubber bands with two-prong hooks at each end, ponytail fashion barrettes of gleaming polished plastic with sponge backs and double-lock fasteners, and large elastic tail holders in assorted colors. The daisy-do ponytail holder has a bright patent look in brilliant-color vinyl, and floral ponytail holders in assorted roses and daisies are witty ways to dress up your hairdo. American Indian leather ponytail holders, complete with bouncy fringe, beaded pearl tail holders clustered on elastic strings, and cat's-eye ponytail holders are some of the newest hair accessories.

Hair Jewelry

Rounding out the collection of Tip-Top hair accessories are the jeweled clips, the charm clips, and the coiffure bands. The jeweled clips come in pairs, and are decorated in either pearls with gold or rhinestones with silver.

HAIR JEWELRY

The charm clips are a bit larger and are sold separately. They are right for that single, dramatic accent. They have an antique finish and come in gold and silver. Fashion barrettes in gold, and the coiffure band which fits the head securely, are lovely hair accessories.

Invisible Coverups

Nylon French mesh hair nets are great for keeping curls where they should be without letting anyone know what's going on. There are nylon nets of French mesh with extra-fine elastic stretch yarn edges. The wave nets are long-wearing, highly protective, and all poly bagged. In addition, there are unseeable open-weave mesh hair nets with elastic edges, made of long-lasting mesh with adjustable drawstrings. Triangular veils, full size for drying hair or sleeping, and hand-tied nets with tiny beads, are also available.

Vinyl Shower Caps

Vinyl shower caps should have a look of fashion, too. There are bouffant-size dotted Swiss or printed nylon tricot caps with ruffled trim and waterproof vinyl lining, and dainty eyelet shower caps with lace trims and elastic edges. The bouffant sizes cover the most complicated coifs. Terry-lined printed vinyl caps with lace trim and elastic edges protect your hair, while keeping you looking your best.

Terry Turbans

Terry cloth is used in the new double-knit terry fashion turbans for after-shampooing and after-swim-

TERRY TURBAN

ming. These turbans are extra soft and extra absorbent. In addition, they are washable and very comfortable to wear. The miracle turban of foam net protects your hairdo day or night, and it fits all heads. The terry hair protector with poly foam lining is ideal under swim caps or shower caps, and is used for applying makeup.

Breeze Bonnets and Scarves

Breeze bonnets have a hoodlike design, bound with ribbon ties. They are made of wispy fabrics, such as nylon tulle and chiffon, and come in a variety of high-fashion colors, as well as black and beige. Some breeze bonnets have gay patterns and others have a sprinkling of glitter.

Nylon scarves, ranging from large squares to longies, are available in a variety of different colors. In addition, special chapel scarves and caps are handy hair coverups. The tiny chapel caps are in black and white lace and have their own carrying cases. The mantilla triangle is nylon lace with a pretty ruffled edge.

The rain scarf looks like a simple triangular scarf and is designed like a hood with ties. Triangles have a sporty look and are easy to wear. Tip-Top's Tri-Toppers are cute and saucy. They come in gay, exciting prints with new and different designs and colors for every season. They always have matching strings that can be tied behind the hair at the nape of the neck or under chin.

Hairdo Savers

To keep your hairdo in place as you sleep, try one of Tip-Top's nylon tricot caps with soft, perforated poly foam linings and adjustable ring tops. Another hairdo saver is the bouffant-size cap that is made of nonwoven, lightweight cotton that has been perforated. It is inexpensive and it keeps your curls in place while you sleep.

Slumber Caps

Coiffure bonnets with adjustable ring tops, and adjustable self-tie curler coverups are two ways to look prettier at bedtime. The coiffure bonnet with adjustable ring top is made of nylon tricot and has matching nylon dotted swiss ruffles. It has a plastic ring that slides up or down to adjust the size of the cap from regular to bouffant so that it can cope with any size rollers. The elastic band holds hair gently, but firmly.

SLUMBER CAP

Satin Sleep Caps

One of the newest innovations in sleep caps is the satin sleep cap. It protects your hair as you sleep, allowing free, easy motion of your hair against the satin finish. Beehive-style caps of nylon chiffon, super bouffant ruffled nylon tricot and embroidered eyelet trim, and nylon fishnet trimmed with cross-dyed lace are also included in the Tip-Top collection of slumber caps. The double-layer tricot caps are soft and light, and conform to the hair set, holding it lightly in place. Because of its bouffant size, the sateena sleep cap with metallic lace overlay allows your hairdo complete freedom.

SATIN SLEEP CAP

TIP-TOP'S 50 PROFESSIONAL
STYLING SECRETS

1. If your hair has a tendency to frizz, remove rollers (without disturbing set) while hair is slightly damp. Cover hair with a loose net until curls are completely dry.

2. King-size clips are used to hold sections away from face when setting. In addition, they are used to mold wide waves into place.

3. Always use end papers with rollers to prevent fish hooks or bent ends.

4. To decorate a ponytail, try a cluster, beaded tail holder, a leather tail with a drawstring, or a fashionable flower holder.

5. In making clip curls, be sure the ends are inside the curl or else you'll get fly-away ends.

6. Fine hair takes best to brush-type rollers. The bristles hold the hair securely for a firmer set.

7. For in-between salon visits, keep a hair trimmer and shaper within easy reach. A 5-inch ruler on the handle is for easy measuring while shaping. It comes with a double-edged blade and is easy to use.

8. To set a synthetic wig, use plastic rollers and water. Be sure to use end papers on clip curls. Cover set with a net and dry under a home dryer.

9. If your hair is very coarse, damaged, or color-treated, try magnetic rollers. This type of hair .gets easily dented and takes better to this kind of roller.

10. Hair jewelry completes the coiffure . . . especially for evening wear. A gold head band or a tortoiseshell barrette can add glamour to a simple hairdo.

11. To clean your comb, swish it in some detergent suds mixed with ammonia. Wash comb after each shampoo.

12. A plastic hair foundation adds body to your coiffure. The plastic hair foundation is available in large, bouffant sizes, and is great for falls, wiglets, or your own hair.

13. Create extra body with your style by backbrushing or teasing. Backbrush hair toward scalp, starting at the ends.

14. Choose the right kind of comb for your hair type. For normal hair, choose an all-purpose comb which graduates from fine to coarse teeth. If your hair is fine or smooth, choose a comb with fine teeth.

15. Make sure the hairspray you use is water-soluble. Rayette's Aqua Net is water-soluble and moisture-controlled for all kinds of weather. Besides, there's no spray build-up.

16. Controllers are brush-type rollers made of plastic. They are as soft as foam rollers, curl like magnetic rollers, and hold like brush rollers. These soft, cush-

iony rollers come in three different sizes, large, jumbo, and medium bouffant.

17. Wet hair is especially fragile. After shampooing, treat it gently by blotting dry with a towel. Never pull or tug the hair.

18. In making clip curls, comb each strand through until it is smooth. This eliminates frizzy ends.

19. To create a quick and easy chignon, use a chignon foundation. A chignon foundation is a circular form of double horsehair braid and elasticized tubing. It is about 3½ inches round and is easy to use.

20. For maximum sleeping comfort, use Tip-Top Comfy Pads—poly foam roller pads with your brush rollers. Or try foam rubber rollers, which are the most comfortable rollers for sleeping.

21. In setting hair, do not wind rollers too tightly. This can harm the hair and cause breakage.

22. For a smoother set, section hair carefully. Follow the setting patterns shown, saturating ends with setting gel. Comb out each section until smooth.

23. Ringlets can be set on small rollers wound in a vertical position, or with bob pins. In using bob pins, make sure they are rubber-tipped to protect the hair.

24. Always protect your hair when out in the sun. A pretty coverup, such as a sports triangle or a scarf, will protect the hair against sun and wind.

25. After washing and rinsing your hair, it should be towel-dried. Hair should be damp (not wet) so the setting gel blends in evenly. Dribble gel on generously through the nozzle with a wide-toothed comb. Use either the normal formula or the hard-to-hold formula.

26. To eliminate any roller marks, set rollers close together. When dry, brush hair out until all roller marks disappear.

27. A two-sided mirror, with magnifying and regular mirrors, is a handy accessory for setting your hair. These mirrors can be used in your vanity, or they can be carried in your purse.

28. Cotton rolls are used to set bouncy bangs. Saturate bangs with setting gel and fill with cotton roll. Tape into place.

29. Wigs, wiglets, and falls should be styled with special wig accessories. A professional wig styler lifts, puffs, styles, smooths, and separates. In addition, there's a rattail handle for added ease. A nonstatic wig styling brush with three rows of bristles can also be used on wigs, falls, and wiglets.

30. Choose the right kind of hairspray to complete your coif. Some hairsprays have built-in conditioners, while others are especially formulated for hard-to-hold hair.

31. To set thick, curly hair, use extra-large rollers and a setting gel to tame ends. Get your hair thinned to reduce the excess bulk, and consider a hair straightening.

32. An important hair accessory today for falls and wiglets is the plastic or nylon foundation. It's great for lifting and holding hair pieces.

33. Never submerge a brush in water. Swish the bristles through sudsy water and rinse. Allow to dry face up.

34. To revive a wilted set, wind your hair on rollers, spraying ends with hairspray. Allow hair to dry thoroughly before combing out.

35. Use pins to make firmer curls. Pin curls are good for hair that is too short to wind on a roller, or for setting tendrils. In addition, a single row of clip curls along the nape gives a style extra bounce.

36. If your hair is very oily, cover your hairbrush with a piece of gauze to pick up excess oils.

37. Generally speaking, jumbo rollers give a smooth, sleek look to long, maxi hair. However, medium to large rollers would be a better choice if your hair is fine and has a tendency to wilt.

38. For dry, tinted, or dull hair, spray hair with a special spray dressing and conditioner. Caryl Richard's Happy Hair has built-in conditioners and makes hair softer and more lustrous-looking.

39. After removing rollers, brush the hair out in the opposite direction of the finished style. This gives your coif more flow and helps hold the lines of the set.

40. Transparent tape can be used to set side guiches and to hold down short hair along the nape of the neck. To set bangs, saturate hair with setting gel and tape into place.

41. To keep brushes clean, wipe bristles after every brushing. Use the end of a comb to remove loose hair.

42. Use a small styling comb to flip ends upward, or the tip of a rattail comb to create layered bangs.

43. Saturate hair with water or setting gel before setting. A setting gel is great for firmer flips and fluffy ruffs.

44. Dry a brush at room temperature or in the fresh air. Never let it dry in the hot sun.

45. Spray your hair lightly after you have finished styling it. In spraying, hold the can at least 10 inches away from the face.

46. For the shorter, curlier hairdos, switch to smaller-size rollers; or longer-lasting curls can be yours with a gentle perm.

47. Fine hair takes best to brush-type rollers. The bristles hold the hair securely in place.

48. Perk up a pretty ponytail by wrapping some twisted yarn ties around it. The yarn ties come in a variety of different colors and add a note of gaiety to pigtails and ponytails.

49. After removing rollers, brush the hair out vigorously. Brushing eliminates the roller marks and gives more springiness to the style.

50. Use a natural bristle brush for everyday hair care. Soft bristles are especially good for tinted or extra-fine hair.

CHAPTER III

55 NEW COIFFURE CREATIONS—FROM THE WORLD'S LEADING HAIR DESIGNERS—COMPLETE WITH SETTING PATTERNS

How to Set and Style the Latest Casuals . . . Convertibles . . . Pages . . . Ponies . . . Pullbacks . . . Pigtails . . . Falls . . . Flips . . . Napehuggers . . . Caps . . . Curls . . . Swirls . . . Hairpieces . . . Wigs . . . Step-by-Step Instruction from Setting to Comb-Out for Each and Every Style

After-Five Formals

Style by Michael Ayervais
Salon East 57th Street, New York

Michael Ayervais of Salon East 57 touches off this party hairdo with tiny flowers. To set, wind jumbo rollers away from center part. Set tendrils on small rollers at the sides of the face and along the napeline. When dry, brush hair out smoothly from part, curving over·ears. Brush hair toward the back, catching ends with a coated elastic band. Using a small styling brush, form ponytail high on crown. Let one curl hang loosely at crown for a feminine finish. Remove small rollers, letting tendrils dangle freely.

After-Five Formals

Style by Jacques Dessanges
Paris, France

Jacques Dessanges is a master at creating elegant evening hairdos. This style is brushed smoothly off the face, ending in a tiny topknot. To set, wind jumbo rollers away from face. Use pincurls to set tiny tendrils along the front hairline, and along the nape of the neck. When dry, brush hair out until smooth. Brush hair toward crown, catching ends with a coated elastic band. Wrap remaining hair, as shown, or top off with a small braided postiche.

After-Five Formals

Style by Federico
Florence, Italy

Federico of Florence takes maxi hair and pulls it back into an artistic arrangement. To set, wind jumbo rollers away from the face. When dry, brush hair out until smooth. Form a circle of pins at the back of the head to hold hair securely in place. Use a small styling brush to form three small chignons. Arrange chignons at the side, and secure with invisible pins.

For a different variation of the chignon, brush hair away from face, catching ends with a coated elastic band. Form a chignon at the nape of the neck, and secure with invisible pins. For added glamour, entwine a small mini-braid around chignon.

After-Five Formals

Style by Femme Sistina
Rome, Italy

A long ponytail is decorated with a circle of pre-shaped pompons. To set, use jumbo rollers throughout. When dry, brush hair away from face until smooth. Catch ends with a coated elastic band, low on the nape of the neck. Use invisible pins to hold hair back. Attach a circle of pompons, pulling through circle, as shown.

For a completely different effect, Femme Sistina sweeps hair away from crown and tops it off with a small chignon. The beauty of this style is in its chic simplicity. To set, follow an all-roller setting. Use large to jumbo rollers throughout. When dry, brush hair out in the lines of the set. Be sure all roller marks are removed. Pin hair away from face. Attach a small chignon of pompons high on the crown.

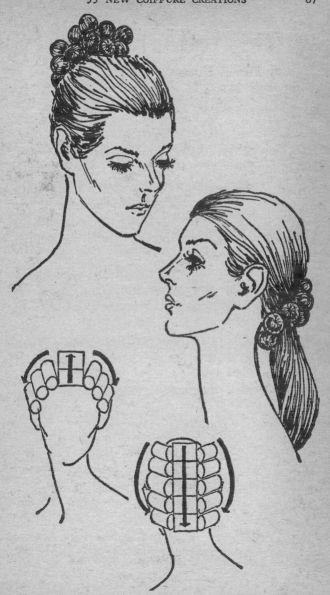

After-Five Formals

Style by Femme Sistina
Rome, Italy

Femme Sistina of Rome, Italy, sets mid-length hair on jumbo rollers, wound away from the face. When dry, brush hair out away from brow until smooth. Be sure all roller marks disappear. Catch ends with a coated elastic band. Attach a cluster of instant curls at back crown for an elegant evening hairdo. The cluster is a high-fashion arrangement of pompons which come pre-styled. Spray lightly to hold hair in place.

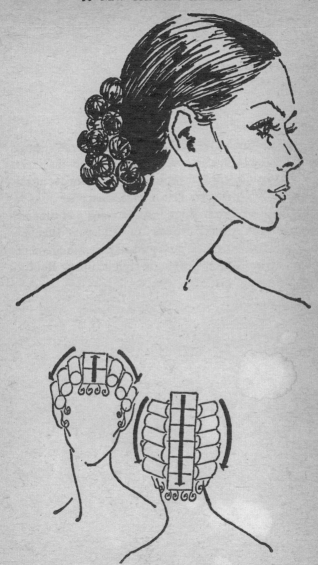

After-Five Formals

Style by Joe of
Ray and Joe's Place
Briarwood, New York

Joe of Ray and Joe's Place arranges loose curls at the side of the face for a romantic, feminine finish. To set, wind large to jumbo rollers away from the side part. When dry, brush hair out in the lines of the set. Backbrush sides for extra height. Smooth crown away from part, securing ends with a decorative barrette. Form corkscrew curls by brushing strands over finger, spraying lightly as you go along.

After-Five Formals

Style by Siro Paglia
Siro's Beauty Salon
Flourtown, Pa.

This ultra-feminine hairdo is swept off the face
into a lovely topknot. Tiny tendrils adorn the front
hairline, extending down the sides and back. To
set, wind jumbo rollers away from the face. Saturate tendrils with setting gel and clip into place.
When dry, brush hair away from crown, leaving
clip curls intact. Gather hair into a ponytail high
on the crown. Form a chignon, turning ends under. Wrap a mini-braid around chignon. Release
clip curls, allowing tendrils to dangle freely.

Beautiful Bobs

Style by Jacques Dessanges
Paris, France

Jacques Dessanges styles long hair into a fluffy bob. To set, wind medium to large rollers out from a side part. Make a triple row of clip curls at the back of the head, and along the sides. Saturate hair with setting gel for a firmer set. When dry, brush hair out in the lines of the set. Backbrush sides. Arrange curls at the sides, as illustrated.

A looser and more dramatic version of this style can be achieved by brushing hair away from face to emphasize perfect contours. Brush the hair out so that the curls fall casually onto the shoulders.

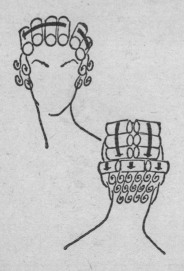

Beautiful Bobs

Style by Filippo of Rome

An expert taper cut is the basis of this beautiful bob by Filippo of Rome. Gentle waves fall over the ears, and along the front hairline. To set, use medium to large rollers throughout. If the back hair is very short, it can be taped into place, or set with pin curls, as shown. When dry, brush hair out from crown, using a forward motion. Backbrush crown and sides. Using a small styling brush, flick bangs upward, bringing side hair over the ears. Spray lightly for the perfect finish.

Beautiful Bobs

Style by Edith Imre
New York City

This stylish bob by Edith Imre features a high side part and soft waves. To set, use small to medium rollers throughout, with a double row of clip curls at the back of the neck. When dry, brush hair out from side part until all roller marks disappear. Using a small styling brush, form deep waves by brushing strands over hand. Arrange hair so that the sides end in a winged effect. Spray lightly to hold waves in place.

Beautiful Bobs

Style by Kenneth
New York City

Finger waves are the basis of this beautiful bob by Kenneth. Hair has been cut to jaw length, and has a high side part. Finger waves, made from an all pin curl pin setting, create the desired effect. When dry, brush hair out from side part. Using a styling brush and the back of the hand, brush hair into deep waves at the sides of the face. Continue making waves across the back of the head. Spray lightly to hold hair in place.

Beautiful Bobs

Style by Alain Mamann
Montreal, Canada

Alain Mamann of Montreal creates a delightful party hairdo by styling mid-length hair into a tiny ponytail with plenty of side interest. To set, saturate bangs with setting gel and tape into place. Use medium to jumbo rollers throughout. When dry, brush out in the lines of the set, catching hair with a coated elastic band. Leave hair free at the sides to form small ringlets. To form curls, brush strands over finger with a small styling brush. Allow curls to dangle freely. Mist lightly with spray.

Beautiful Bobs

Style by Michel of Paris
New York City

This charming hairdo by Michel of Paris is layered and taper-cut at ear level. Set front on large
rollers, using jumbo rollers for back. Make a double
row of clip curls at the nape of the neck. When
dry, brush hair out in the direction of the set. Backbrush crown for extra height. Brush bangs out at
an angle, flicking ends upward with a small styling
brush. Brush side guiches toward cheeks.

Beautiful Bobs

Style by Siro Paglia
Siro's Beauty Salon
Flourtown, Pa.

This delightful bob combines smooth bangs with a ruff of curls. To set, saturate bangs with setting gel and tape into place. Use jumbo rollers throughout with a single row of clip curls at the nape of the neck. Note the vertical placement of rollers at the back of the head. Backbrush sides and back. Using a small styling brush, brush strands over finger. Mist lightly to hold curls in place.

Carefree Casuals

Style by Jacques Dessanges
Paris, France

Jacques Dessanges styles mid-length hair into a simple, natural style. To set, wind jumbo rollers away from face. When dry, brush hair out until all roller marks are removed. Backbrush entire head lightly. (If your hair is fine, a body wave will give it extra fullness.) Brush hair out in the lines of the set, swirling the brush as you go along. Mist hair lightly with a gentle hairspray.

Carefree Casuals

Style by Siro Paglia
Siro's Beauty Salon
Flourtown, Pa.

This short, curly coif has been carefully tapered by Siro Paglia of Flourtown, Pa. Open curls and dramatic streaks accent its loveliness. Set hair on medium to large rollers throughout, with a double row of clip curls at the nape of the neck. When dry, brush hair out in the lines of the set. For extra fullness, backbrush entire head with a small teasing brush. Curve bangs onto forehead, pulling side guiches onto face. Brush strands over finger to form individual curls.

Casual Coifs

Style by Linda Ballard of Richmond, Va.

This classic style by Linda Ballard of Richmond, Va. features deeply curved bangs and full sides which extend slightly below jaw level. To set, use jumbo rollers throughout, with a single row of clip curls at the nape of the neck. Note the vertical placement of rollers at the back of the head which gives it the necessary swing. When dry, brush hair out from side part, sweeping bangs low onto brow. Backbrush sides for extra volume. Use a small styling brush to create the soft lines of this style, curving ends under. Spray lightly.

Casual Coifs

Style by Jacques Dessanges
Paris, France

This pageboy takes on a brand new look with sweep bangs and full sides which gently turn under. Medium-length hair is blunt cut and set on jumbo to large rollers throughout. Wind rollers away from side part, turning rollers at side under. Bangs have been saturated with setting gel for a firmer finish. When dry, brush hair out from side part, and secure with invisible pins. Backbrush crown and sides for extra volume. Brush hair out until smooth, curving ends under.

Casual Coifs

Style by Federico
Florence, Italy

Federico of Florence layer-cuts this brief casual coif. To set, saturate hair with setting gel, using medium rollers, as shown. Make a triple row of clip curls at the back of the head. When dry, run hair through fingers to loosen set. Tease hair gently with a small styling brush, or try a gentle perm if your hair lacks body. Brush hair out at sides, curving guiches onto face. Use the tip of a rattail comb to create a layered look.

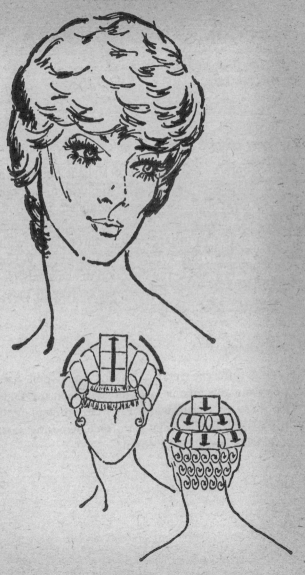

Casual Coifs

Style by John Fonda
New York City

For Day

John Fonda creates a Prince Valiant cut with a horizontal part at the center of the crown. Smooth bangs and gentle curved ends complete the look. To set, saturate bangs with setting gel, and tape into place. Use jumbo to large rollers throughout, with a single row of tiny rollers at the napeline. When dry, brush hair out in the direction of the set. Back-brush sides and back, turning ends under in page-boy fashion. Mist lightly.

For Evening

For a different version of this style, pull hair away from the face at back crown, securing ends with a coated elastic band. Encircle ponytail with a ring. Brush hair at sides onto face, exposing ears. Comb back hair straight down.

Casual Coifs

Style by Paul Mitchell
The Crimpers
New York City

Paul Mitchell cuts shoulder-length hair into a light, feathery style. Straight bangs are offset by a flurry of casual curls. To set, saturate bangs with setting gel and tape into place. Use jumbo rollers throughout with a single row of clip curls at the nape of the neck. When dry, brush hair out in the direction of the set. Brush bangs straight down, forming curls at the sides of the face by brushing strands over finger with a small styling brush.

Chic Classics

Style by Antonio of
Maria Rei Beauty Salon
New York City

Antonio of Maria Rei in New York dresses up a midi-fall by wrapping a small mini-braid around the crown, looping it at mid-center. The basic flip is set on jumbo rollers, wound away from the face. The rollers at the sides are wound in a downward direction. For a firmer flip, saturate ends with setting lotion. Set tendrils on small rollers, or make clip curls, as shown. When dry, brush hair out in the lines of the set until crown is completely smooth. Attach midi-fall at back crown. Using a small styling brush, flick ends upward. Tie mini-braid around crown to conceal joining.

Chic Classics

Style by Julius Caruso
of New York City

Julius Caruso takes mid-length hair and pulls it away from the face for maximum back interest. To set, use medium to jumbo rollers throughout, with smaller rollers at the nape of the neck. When dry, brush hair away from the face. Backbrush back and crown with a small teasing brush. Pull hair back at sides and secure with invisible pin. Allow hair at crown to fall over back hair into a large wave. Brush hair under at back into a smooth pageboy. Accent back with a hair bow, flower, or barrette.

Chic Classics

Style by Siro Paglia
Siro's Beauty Salon
Flourtown, Pa.

Day

Siro styles long, maxi hair with a center part and gently upturned ends. This all-time classic for long hair features deep waves at the sides of the face to balance a perfect silhouette. To set, wind jumbo rollers away from the center part. When dry, brush hair out, forming deep waves at the sides with a styling brush and the back of the hand. Curve hair toward face at sides, using a small styling brush to flick ends upward.

Evening

For an evening look, Siro sweeps the hair away from the center part, creating a smooth crown. Tendrils are reset on small rollers for a feminine finish. Form a circle of pins to hold the hair back. Divide the back hair in several sections. Using a small styling brush, make large curls by brushing wide strands over finger. Secure with invisible pins. Remove small rollers, allowing tendrils to dangle freely.

Chic Classics

Style by Valentino of Italy

This fabulous flip by Valentino has been frosted for added glamour. To set, use large to jumbo rollers throughout. A triple row of clip curls at the back of the neck creates more firmness. When dry, brush hair out in the direction of the set, swirling brush upward as you go along. Backbrush gently for extra volume. Using a professional beautician's brush, form deep wave onto the forehead by brushing hair over the back of the hand. Flick ends upward with a small styling brush.

Marvelous Maxis

Style by Antonio of
Maria Rei Beauty Salon
New York City

Antonio styles long maxi hair so that it is pulled over to one side, and left to drape over the shoulder. A thick hank of hair is wrapped over the ponytail, forming a self-knot. To set, use jumbo rollers throughout, with smaller rollers at the nape of the neck. Be sure that rollers are wound in a downward direction. When dry, brush hair out from side part until it falls smoothly over the forehead. Secure hair with a coated elastic band, leaving one thick hank of hair free. Form self-knot around ponytail, draping remaining hair over shoulder.

Marvelous Maxis

Style by Julius Caruso
of New York City

Julius Caruso pulls maxi hair away from the face and knots it into a youthful ponytail. To set, use jumbo rollers throughout. Be sure to wind front three rollers away from face. When dry, brush hair out until smooth. Brush back hair into a smooth ponytail, catching ends with a coated elastic band. Form a self-knot by winding a wide hank of hair around ponytail.

Marvelous Maxis

Style by Julius Caruso
of New York City

Day

Julius Caruso combines a sleek crown with a ruff of curls. Hair is blunt-cut at shoulder level. To set, wind rollers out from a center part, as shown. Hair at crown has been saturated with water and combed out smoothly close to head. Use medium to large rollers throughout. A single row of clip curls is made at the nape of the neck. When dry, remove rollers and clip curls, brushing hair out in the lines of the set. For a more definite silhouette, form a circle of pins around the head. Using a small styling brush, form individual curls by brushing strands over finger. Spray lightly as you go along.

Evening

For a variation of the same style, brush hair away from crown until smooth, sweeping hair over ears. Catch ends with a coated elastic band. Secure with invisible pins. Using a small styling brush, brush strands over finger, forming curls low on nape.

Marvelous Maxis

Style by Joe
Ray and Joe's Place
Briarwood, New York

This long, shaggy look combines tapered sides and casual bangs. A body wave gives softness and long-lasting waves. To set, wind medium to large rollers throughout, with a double row of clip curls at the nape of the neck. When dry, run fingers through hair to loosen set. Brush hair out in the direction of the set. Backbrush sides and back for extra fullness. Arrange waves, as shown.

To vary this style, divide hair in half at the back of the head. Catch ends with coated elastic bands. Cover bands with decorative bows. Use the tip of a rattail comb to create feathered bangs. Brush pigtails out so that the ends fall gently onto the shoulders.

Marvelous Maxis

Style by Michel of Paris
New York City

Michel of Paris takes long, maxi hair and pulls it back into an eye-catching ponytail. To set, wind jumbo rollers away from face, with a few clip curls at front hairline. Use large to jumbo rollers for the back setting, with a single row of clip curls at the nape of the neck. When dry, brush hair away from crown until smooth, making sure all roller marks disappear. Catch ends with a coated elastic band. Divide ponytail into two sections, winding one section over the other, as shown in sketch. Secure with invisible pins. Brush ponytail out until smooth. Remove clip curls, brushing tendrils toward face and onto cheeks.

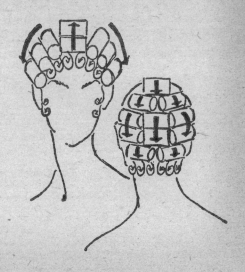

Marvelous Maxis

Style by Siro Paglia
Siro's Beauty Salon
Flourtown, Pa.

This soft, feminine ponytail is the creation of Siro Paglia of Flourtown, Pa. Hair has been blunt cut all one length. To set, wind jumbo rollers away from face. When dry, brush hair out until all roller marks disappear. Catch ends with a coated elastic band high on crown. Use invisible pins to hold ends securely in place. Brush ponytail out with a small styling brush. Spray lightly. Decorate ponytail with an elaborate velvet bow.

Marvelous Maxis

Style by Maria Rei
Maria Rei Beauty Salon
New York City

Day

Maria Rei's "lion look" has been tapered to fall beneath the shoulders. For longer-lasting curls, Maria suggests a gentle perm. To set, use jumbo rollers throughout, rolling hair at the nape of the neck, as indicated. When dry, run fingers through hair to loosen set. Backbrush entire head for extra volume. Using a small styling brush, arrange hair into a bevy of curls. Use fingers to bring hair forward at the crown and along the sides.

Evening .

A different comb-out will transfer this free-flowing mane into a chic chignon. Brush hair away from face until smooth. Bring hair toward the back, catching ends with a coated elastic band. Divide ponytail in half. Take one section and wrap it around the other section, forming a chic chignon. Repeat procedure for the other section. Secure with invisible pins. Spray lightly.

Nifty Napehuggers

Style by Antonio of
Maria Rei Beauty Salon
New York City

Day

This delightful day-style requires only four rollers, as shown. Note the direction of the arrows in the diagram. The bangs and nape have been saturated with setting lotion and taped into place. When dry, brush hair out from mid-crown onto brow. Long sideburns are brushed straight down, close to the face.

Evening

For evening, set a small wiglet on medium rollers. When dry, brush hair out until all roller marks disappear, forming individual curls with a small styling brush. Attach wiglet at back crown. Spray lightly.

Nifty Napehuggers

Style by Jacques Dessanges
Paris, France

This nape-hugging style has chin-length hair at the sides, casual bangs, and gentle nape curls. To set, saturate bangs and guiches with water or styling gel, and tape into place. For bouncier bangs, use a jumbo roller. Wind two medium-size rollers at the nape of the neck in an upward direction. When dry, brush hair out in the lines of the set, using a small styling brush to flick ends upward.

Nifty Napehuggers

Style by Alain Mamann
Montreal, Canada

Day

Alain Mamann of Montreal favors long sideburns and gentle waves. This close-to-the-head style depends upon a professional layer cut. To set, use jumbo rollers, as shown, taping banks and hair along nape of neck into place. Reverse guiches are also taped into place. When dry, brush hair out, using short strokes. Backbrush crown and back for extra height. Use the tip of a rattail comb to create a layered look. Fan hair out at the nape of the neck. Brush reverse guiches out in a downward direction.

Evening

For evening, add a few wispy pin-on curls at the nape of the neck. Pin the curls on individually, so that you have a long, shaggy look. Make sure the ends are tapered for a light, see-through appearance.

Nifty Napehuggers

Style by the Roman Empire Hairstylists
Toronto, Canada

The Roman Empire Hairstylists in Toronto create a casual forward-moving coif for daytime wear.
To set, use large rollers throughout, with a double
row of clip curls at the back of the neck. When
dry, brush hair out from mid-crown, swirling brush
toward face. Arrange hair in a face-framing fringe
around face, as shown. Use the tip of a rattail comb
to create a feathered effect.

Nifty Napehuggers

Style by Vidal Sassoon
New York City

This casual cut by Vidal Sassoon has been gently permed for extra volume. The hair, as a result, has a thick, full look, which depends upon expert brushwork. To set, wind jumbo rollers away from face. Tape sideburns into place, as well as hair along the nape of the neck. When dry, brush hair away from face so that the brow is exposed. Using a professional beautician's brush, swirl brush as you go along, forming deep, casual waves throughout. Brush sideburns out, fanning them toward face. Brush hair out along the nape of the neck so that it has a feathered, casual look.

Ponies, Pigtails and Pulls

Style by Enrico Caruso
New York City

This pretty pullback by Enrico Caruso of New York features a center part and long, feminine curls. To set, use jumbo rollers throughout, with clip curls at the sides and along the nape of the neck. When dry, brush hair out from a center part, leaving the clip curls in place. Make a circle of bob pins at the back to hold hair in place. Backbrush hair gently for extra volume. Form large curls with a small styling brush. Wind strands around finger, spraying as you go along. Bring one long curl forward.

Ponies, Pigtails and Pulls

Style by Pam Geiger
Edith Imre Salon
New York City

This pretty pullback by Pam Geiger of Edith Imre features two long braids which fall onto the shoulders, and looped mini-braids. To set, wind jumbo rollers away from the face. Use small rollers at the nape of the neck. When dry, brush hair out in the lines of the set, catching ends with a coated elastic band low at the nape. Gather hair at nape and divide into three sections. Braid each section. Secure ends of each tail with a coated elastic band. Decorate the ends with hair jewelry. Make an arrangement of looped mini-braids and secure at back crown.

Ponies, Pigtails and Pulls

Style by Victor Morley

A dramatic, center-parted style, is Victor Morley's answer to maxi hair. To set, wind jumbo rollers out from side part. The hair has been blunt cut all one length. When dry, brush hair out from center part, until smooth. Attach a fall of casual curls high on the crown, and brush to one side.

For a completely different look, brush hair away from crown, catching ends with a coated elastic band. Attach a free-flowing arrangement of curls at the crown. Conceal joining with a tiny mini-braid. Hairpiece designs by Victor Morley.

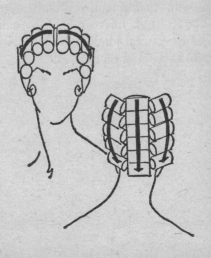

Pretty Put-Ons

Style by Femme Sistina
Rome, Italy

This long, flowing ponytail by Femme Sistina coils upward for maximum drama. To set, use jumbo rollers throughout. Be sure to wind front rollers away from the face. When dry, brush hair out until crown is smooth. Form a circle of pins at the lower nape. Attach pin-on "Lazy Tail" and presto . . . a new you. (The Lazy Tail requires no setting . . . it is pre-curled.)

The same hairpiece accessory can be used to create two ponytails at the sides of the face. For the comb-out, make a center part, brushing hair out until smooth. Catch hair on both sides with a coated-elastic band. Leave a hank of hair free on both sides to conceal joining. Attach pin-on ponytails. Form a self-knot on each side.

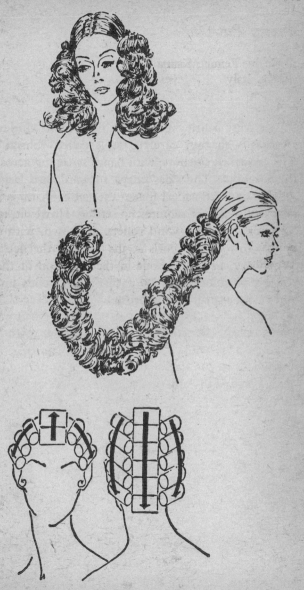

Pretty Put-Ons

Style by Victor Morley

The Miss Morley Collection by Victor Morley features a shaggy, carefree look called "Shatzi." The crown is cut short, with bangs sweeping across the forehead. The sides curve forward into large guiches and the nape caresses the neck. Shatzi is a synthetic wig that requires no setting. However, to set your own hair, wind rollers, as shown, with a double row of clip curls at the back of the neck. When dry, brush hair out in the direction of the set. Brush guiches toward face, flicking ends upward with a small styling brush.

Pretty Put-Ons

Style by Victor Morley

Victor Morley's carefree coif has fluid lines and plenty of movement. Saturate hair with setting gel before winding on rollers. Wind medium rollers out from side part, making a triple row of clip curls at the nape of the neck. The clip curls will give the set extra firmness. When dry, brush hair out in the lines of the set. Sweep hair toward side at front hairline. Backbrush back and sides for extra volume. Use a small styling brush to form casual curls.

Pretty Put-Ons

Style by Tony Al Parliamento
Rome, Italy

This special-occasion hairdo by Tony Al Parliamento of Rome features lots of ringlets and a curly topknot. To set, use medium to large rollers throughout. Saturate bangs with water and tape into place. Set tendrils on small rollers. When dry, brush bangs out until smooth. Using a small teasing brush, backbrush hair at sides and back. Form ringlets by brushing strands over finger. Allow curls to dangle freely onto the shoulders.

Sensational Shorties

Style by Linda Ballard of Richmond, Va.

Linda Ballard of Richmond, Va. creates this charming mini-coif by creating a bevy of casual curls all over the head. To set, use medium to large rollers throughout, taping back into place. When dry, brush hair out in the direction of the set. Back-brush crown, sides and back. Use a small styling brush to create curls by brushing strands over finger. Spray lightly to hold curls in place.

Sensational Shorties

Style by Carita of Paris

Day

This small, close-to-the-head look by Carita of Paris has light, springy curls and baby locks. The cherub cut has been scissor-cut, leaving very fine, almost transparent ends. The length of the hair varies from ¼ inch at the front to 2 inches at the nape of the neck. For best results with this style, Carita suggests a gentle perm. To set, use small rollers throughout. When dry, run fingers through hair to loosen set. Brush hair vigorously, swirling brush as you go along.

Evening

For evening, Carita tops off this charming hairdo with narrow chignons. The chignons are encased in little metal nets, or stylized with some accessory. For a special evening out, Carita pins on wild flowers, daisies, poppies, honeysuckle, cornflowers, and forget-me-nots.

Sensational Shorties

Style by Joseph Febbrini
Bellisima,
Dallas, Texas

Day

Joseph Febbrini of Bellisima in Dallas, Texas, sets this style on medium-to-large rollers throughout, with a double row of clip curls at the back of the neck. Clip curls are placed at each side of the face, and along the front hairline. When dry, brush hair out in the direction of the set. Swirl hair as you brush, forming a casual, carefree look. Pull down several strands over front hairline. Flick ends upward. Use the tip of a rattail comb to create a layered look.

Evening

For evening, brush hair toward back, fanning out sideburns. Brush nape hair back, attaching a tiny ponytail. Tie ponytail with a pretty bow.

Sensational Shorties

Style by Joe of
Ray and Joe's Place
Briarwood, New York

This soft, curly coif is Joe's approach to the mini-bob. To set, use small rollers throughout. When dry, run fingers through hair to loosen set. Using a small styling brush, brush strands over finger to form curls. Brush bangs onto forehead into a feminine arrangement of curls.

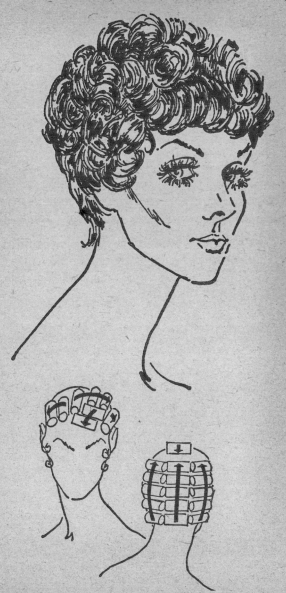

Sensational Shorties

Style by Mr. Joseph
Mr. Joseph's, New York City

Mr. Joseph tapers hair in long layers. To set, wind jumbo rollers away from side part. Saturate bangs and hair along the napeline with water. Tape into place. When dry, brush hair out until all roller marks disappear. Using a small teasing brush, back-brush each section. Use a rattail comb to create a layered effect. As you brush, be sure to swirl brush from left to right, fanning hair out at the nape of the neck.

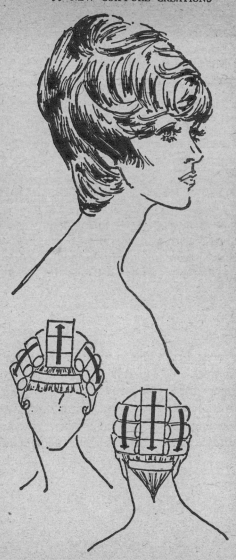

The Super Cuts

Style by Charles Booth
Le Cartier Hair Styles
Montreal, Canada

Day

Baby-fine hair takes to this curly coif. The entire head has been set on small rollers. Three rows of clip curls finish off the setting. When dry, remove rollers, running fingers through hair to loosen set. Backbrush with a small styling brush. Pull curls forward, as shown in sketch. Individual curls are formed by brushing each curl over finger. Spray lightly.

Evening

For evening, brush hair away from brow, setting tendrils at sides on small rollers. Backbrush top for extra height. Brush hair away from face, catching ends with a coated elastic band. Form ringlets with a small styling brush. Arrange curls, as shown. Spray lightly. Draw out cheek and neck tendrils.

The Super Cuts

Style by Pedro Lamas
The Reapers, New York

Pedro Lamas of New York styles long, maxi hair into a bevy of beautiful curls. The hair has been set on medium to large rollers throughout, with a triple row of clip curls at the nape of the neck. When dry, brush hair out in the lines of the set, backbrushing each curl as you go along. Using a small styling brush, form curls by brushing strands over finger. Spray lightly to hold curls in place.

The Super Cuts

Style by Paul Mitchell
The Crimpers, New York

This wash 'n' wear hairdo requires practically no set. The style, created by Paul Mitchell, reaches shoulder length, and features feathered sides and bangs. Saturate hair with water, and brush toward face. Tape bangs, sides, and hair at the nape of the neck into place. When dry, brush hair out in the lines of the set, fanning ends forward. Brush hair onto cheeks, curving ends gently at the nape. Use the tip of a rattail comb to separate and feather ends.

The Super Cuts

Style by Paul Mitchell
The Crimpers, New York

Day

This super cut by Paul Mitchell is short in front and longer at the sides and back. To set, saturate bangs with setting gel and fill with cotton roll. Tape bangs into place. When dry, brush hair out vigorously until all roller marks disappear. Back-brush crown and sides for extra volume, using a small teasing brush. Brush bangs toward face, turning ends under.

Evening

The feathered look comes on strong for after-five. This style requires practically no setting. Saturate hair with setting lotion, taping bangs and hair at nape of neck in place. When dry, remove tape, and brush hair forward. Use the tip of a rattail comb to create a feathered look.

The Super Cuts

Style by the Roman Empire Hairstylists
Toronto, Canada

Day

The serf comes on strong in this super style by the Roman Empire Hairstylists in Toronto, Canada. Cut to shape, this style follows a very simple setting pattern. Set bangs, sides, and back on jumbo rollers, as shown. Wind rollers in a downward direction. When dry, brush hair out until smooth, curving ends under.

Evening

For evening, brush hair down, leaving a separation for the ears. Take a long strand of hair at the back and curl with a heated curling iron. Add a few additional curls at the sides for a dressier effect.

The Super Cuts

Style by Vidal Sassoon
New York City

Vidal Sassoon cuts mid-length hair so that the nape and sides are finely tapered. The hair is swept from a high side part, and accented with tiny tendrils at the sides of the face, and along the nape of the neck. To set, saturate hair with setting lotion, taping hair at the nape of the neck. Make clip curls at sides and along napeline, as shown. When dry, brush hair out until smooth, leaving clip curls in place. Remove clips, forming small guiches and nape coils with finger.

CHAPTER IV

LET'S FACE IT!

Basic Face Shapes and the Hairdos to Match . . .
Styles for the Oval Face . . . Diamond Face . . .
Triangular Face . . . Round Face . . . Square Face
. . . Oblong Face . . . Heart-Shaped Face . . .
Hairdo Tricks to Camouflage a High Forehead . . .
Prominent Nose . . . Too Short Nose . . . Dominant Chin . . . Receding Chin

LET'S FACE IT!

Hair can balance a less-than-perfect face by emphasizing your good features and minimizing your bad features. The shape of your face is of great importance in selecting the right hairdo. If it's oval . . . lucky you! Your problems are nil! However, if you're like most of us, you have either a diamond face, a triangular face, a round face, a square face, an oblong face, or a heart-shaped face.

In addition, you may even have a problem with a high forehead . . . a prominent nose . . . a short nose . . . a dominant chin . . . or a receding chin. However, if you select the right hairdo, you can camouflage your facial faults and create the illusion of a more oval silhouette.

On the pages that follow, we'll tell you all about the basic face shapes and the hairdos to match, as well as all the hairdo tricks to camouflage a large nose, a small nose, sunken-in cheeks, a high forehead, a receding chin, and a dominant chin.

BASIC FACE SHAPES AND THE HAIRDOS TO MATCH

The Oval Face

The oval face is the ideal face shape. If you've been blessed with it, lucky you! Learn how to accentuate your facial contours. The oval face can wear practically any hairdo. Off-the-face styles and center parts emphasize perfect contours. You can choose from smooth, chic styles to curly, casual cuts. The choice is up to you.

The Round Face

The round face is short and broad. Full cheeks are often a problem. To break up the rounded contours, choose a style with height at the top and closeness at the sides. Uneven, swirly effects create a slimmer silhouette.

The Square Face

The width of the forehead and jawline of the square face is about the same. Choose a style with smooth, sleek lines and fullness at the top. Stay away from flat bangs and short, mini-bobs. Soft waves along the forehead and swirls soften the silhouette.

The Oblong Face

The oblong face is long and narrow. To shorten the length, choose a style with soft curls or waves and fullness at the sides. A rounded hairline and chin-length hair enhance this facial type. Avoid exaggerated tops and long, skinny hairdos.

The Triangular Face

The triangular face has a low forehead and a wide jaw. To balance the face, choose a style with fullness at the top. Keep the fullness above the ears, and avoid any flat tops. Styles with softness across the forehead look best.

The Diamond Face

The diamond face has broad cheekbones and a pointed chin. To soften the facial contours, select a style that adds width at chin level. Stay away from center parts. Use bangs to camouflage the front hairline and add width.

The Heart-Shaped Face

The heart-shaped face is wide at the top and narrow at the bottom. If you're lucky, you may even have a widow's peak. To balance this facial shape, add width and fullness at jaw level. Pageboys and flips are especially attractive. Avoid any exaggerated top interest, and keep hair at crown relatively smooth. You can cut the width by curving hair onto the face at cheekbone level. Stay away from off-the-face styles.

BALANCING YOUR FACIAL FEATURES

Your hair can also be used to balance your facial features. Do you have a problem with a large nose . . .

a small nose . . . a receding chin . . . a dominant chin . . . full cheeks . . . sunken-in cheeks? All these facial faults can be camouflaged with the right hairdo.

To minimize a large nose, balance your face with a hairdo that masses the hair at the back. In addition, don't clutter up the face with lots of tiny tendrils and curls. Fluffy bangs also help.

To play up a small nose, wear a mini-bob with casual curls, or a long style with plenty of facial fringe. A receding chin gains in importance with a hairdo that is full at the back and sides, whereas a prominent chin diminishes in size with a style that adds width above the ears. For full cheeks, select a style that curves onto the face, cutting the width of the cheeks. On the other hand, fluffy sides can curve onto the face to cover up sunken-in cheeks.

Bangs, of course, can easily disguise a very high forehead, and an off-the-face hairdo will offset a low forehead or emphasize a widow's peak. In addition, if you wear eyeglasses, stay away from styles that are too severe or fluffy. Stick to styles that emphasize soft, full lines at the top.

CHAPTER V

THE MAKEUP PICTURE

Skin Care: A Complete Guide: Combination/Normal Skin, Dry and/or Sensitive Skin, Oily Skin, Problem Skin and Acne . . . New Techniques with Foundations, Powders, Cheek Colors, Eye Makeup, Lipsticks, and Lashes . . . How to Use Makeup to Correct Certain Problems: Contouring with Makeup

THE MAKEUP PICTURE

Your face says a lot about you. It speaks of your personality without words. The glint of your eyes, the turn of your mouth, the shape of your cheeks all tell something about you. And that's why the care of your skin and the knowledge of the right makeup is so important. You can have a beautiful complexion by knowing your skin type and how to care for it.

Skin Care: A Complete Guide

There are three basic skin types: *Combination/Normal*, *Dry* and *Oily*. And there are different ways to care for each skin type. On the following pages, we will tell you how to cleanse, moisturize, condition and make up your skin so it looks and feels its best. In addition, you'll be able to pick up some pointers on such problems as sensitive skin and acne.

Combination/Normal Skin

Most people think they have normal skin whereas in actuality they have a combination skin type. This complexion is a combination of oily skin with enlarged pores through the forehead, nose and chin area but somewhat dry throughout the rest of the face and throat. This skin type must be treated as two separate skin types and you must use products designed to meet each area's specific needs to bring them into equal balance. This means you should follow a skin routine which involves a moisturizing cream, a skin freshener, and a nourishing cream. Wash the skin with a gentle soap or special cleanser which washes off with water. Apply cold cream or a light moisture cream, and allow it to remain on the face a few minutes. Follow up with a skin toner or refresher on oily areas only. Before retiring, apply a light night cream, and use a special lubricating lotion around the eyes.

Dry and/or Sensitive Skin

Dry skin is parched, sometimes flaky. It has an early tendency to line and wrinkle. When sensitive, it looks red and is prone to blotchiness. This skin type needs almost constant softening, moisturizing, lubricating. This means you should follow a skin routine which involves rich moisturizers and repeated lubrication. In the morning, wash your face with a gentle glycerine soap and warm water. Use a rich day cream underneath your makeup to protect the skin. In addition, apply a moisturizer daily after cleansing the skin, or a special lotion formulated for dry skin. In the evening, cleanse the face with a cleansing cream or lotion, massaging it gently into the face. Close the pores with cool water or a gentle toner. Apply a rich moisturizing night cream before retiring, and use a special lubricating eye cream daily to take care of this extra-sensitive dry area. If your skin is extremely sensitive, prone to allergic reactions, you must use hypoallergenic products or consult a skin doctor.

Oily Skin

This skin type has a shiny, greasy appearance. In addition, it is usually plagued by blackheads and enlarged pores. In such cases, you should follow a skin routine of constant and thorough cleansing, toning and light moisturizing. Frequent washing with an antibacterial soap or cleanser is required to help check surface oiliness. Daily skin care should include a stimulating skin tonic or astringent to tighten the pores. Before retiring, apply a cleansing cream to remove makeup and grime, tissue off and follow with an astringent. However, be sure to use an eye cream around the eyes, as this area has a tendency to dry out even if your skin is oily. In addition, watch your diet carefully, being sure to avoid too many sweets and greasy foods. And, drink at least 8 to 10 glasses of water daily.

Acne

Acne is usually a problem for most teen-agers. Even in its mildest form, acne can mark your skin with blackheads, pimples and whiteheads. To keep it under control, wash your face at least three or four times a day. Use a special antiseptic soap for this purpose, and be sure your hands are washed thoroughly before massaging with fingertips. Massage soap gently onto the face, rinsing off thoroughly with lukewarm water. Follow a balanced diet, avoiding chocolate, fatty foods, soft drinks, and other troublemaking foods. Be sure to get plenty of rest, and don't forget about your exercise. For serious cases of acne, see your dermatologist.

Fabergé makes a whole line of skin treatment products to help protect and correct every skin type. One particular product in their new Xanadu line, is available in three basic formulas, each specifically suited to individual skin types. It's called Xana-Dew Protein-Enriched Complexion Cream . . . a precisely balanced concentrate to coddle the skin by helping to provide the vital balance of natural elements. It is compounded in three densities, each carefully metered to do the most for your skin. Stop by your favorite store and ask for it.

New Techniques with Foundations, Powders, Cheek Colors, Eye Makeup, Lipsticks, and Lashes

Today's woman has the look of natural beauty. Her face is contoured with shaders, highlighters, and blushers, but you'd never know it . . . by the completely natural finish. Eyes are enhanced by following the same principle of contouring, and lips are tinted with see-through colors and transparent glossers.

Eyes, in particular, are in the beauty spotlight. Eyeshadows are used to contour the eye and create different illusions. Shadows are used to brighten, enhance, and deepen the eye. Creamy eye shadows are applied before the face is dusted with powder, whereas other types of shadows are applied afterwards.

For the newest look in eye makeup, use a pale tone for the eyebone area directly beneath the brow, a color which blends in or contrasts with the natural eye color on the lid, and a shader for the crease in the lid. For evening, try one of the frosteds. Mascara is applied after the eyeliner or following the application of false lashes. You can choose from brush-on types, creams, cakes, and lash builders. The new roll-on mascaras are very easy to use, and if you haven't tried false lashes . . . what are you waiting for?

How to Use Makeup to Correct Certain Problems: Contouring with Makeup

Contouring with makeup refers to the use of highlights and shadows to create the illusion of beauty. Contouring can be achieved through the proper use of foundations, shaders, highlighters, blushers, and powders.

Highlighters and Shaders

Highlighters are used to emphasize and enhance certain features. In addition, they correct and minimize flaws. For example, if you use a lighter shade foundation around your eyes, this will cover up any dark circles. As a result, your eyes will appear larger and brighter. On the other hand, if you use a darker shade foundation along the sides of your face, you will create a more oval silhouette. Shading can also be used to camouflage unattractive jowls and double chins.

If your face is too round, apply a white highlighter or a lighter foundation on the cheekbone areas to emphasize bone structure. Sculpture the face by applying a blusher or darker foundation along the sides. This same shader can be used to minimize a dominant chin, jowls, or a double chin. However, be sure to blend the shader evenly so that there is no line of demarcation.

If you want to diminish sunken-in cheeks, use a lighter foundation or white highlighter over your foundation. The hollows will fill out and diminish. A receding chin gains in importance by the careful blending of highlighter or a lighter foundation. On the other hand, a double chin diminishes in size when you apply a dark blusher or a darker foundation underneath the jawline. In addition, a muscular neck seems less prominent if you use a darker shade foundation from the jawbone to the collarbone. Blend in the foundation thoroughly so there is no apparent difference in shading.

The principle that light emphasizes and dark diminishes can also be applied to contouring with eye makeup. You can change the contour of your eye by following these simple eye tricks:

For too small eyes—Use pale shadow and a thin line of eyeliner on the upper lid.

For too heavy eyelids—Use a darker shade of makeup on lids over regular shade.

For too deep-set eyes—Use a light eye makeup on eyelid.

For too close eyes—Use a white eye makeup between inner corners of the eyes.

Corrective makeup can be used to diminish the size of a large nose by applying the highlighter under each eye, and if you have too protruding a forehead, blend the shadow over the entire forehead to make it recede.

However, before you can do any contouring, you must know how to apply foundation makeup correctly. The most important thing to remember is that it should be applied evenly over the entire face and throat so that there is no line of demarcation. Every part of your face, which includes your lips, your eyelids, and your nostrils, should be covered with a light coat of foundation.

Outlined below are some helpful hints and new techniques in makeup:

1. Always begin your makeup with a moisturizer or light cream. It makes your foundation go on easier . . . helps protect your skin from the drying effects of sun and wind.

2. Apply pressed powder by smoothing it on with a clean puff and letting it remain there for a few minutes. Set with a damp sponge.

3. The use of a cheek blusher or face gel can add a glowy healthy-look to your face. Put a little color on your forehead, cheeks and chin for a natural looking blush.

4. The application of a white highlighter or lighter foundation on the cheekbone areas will give an oval look to a round face.

5. Shading or the use of darker foundations will camouflage unattractive jowls and a double chin.

6. To diminish the width of a broad face, apply blusher or dark shading in a wide triangle at the sides of the face.

7. Use a darker foundation along the ridge of the nose to tone down flaring nostrils.

8. Eye whitener can be used to reduce puffiness, circles, and dark shadows under the eyes. First apply whitener, and then apply foundation.

9. For droopy eyes, use pale shadow on the lids, contouring with a darker shade.

10. To tame down unruly brows, brush lightly with baby oil. Use a special eyebrow brush to keep in place.

11. For a soft, natural look in eyebrows, be sure to use a brush-on brow makeup. If you prefer an eyebrow pencil, use short feathery strokes.

12. If you're going to use false eyelashes, apply about ¼ inch from outer corner. Let adhesive dry 60 seconds before applying. Apply mascara to blend in lashes with your own.

13. If human hair lashes lose their curve, re-curl lashes on a pencil that has been wrapped in tissue.

14. Lip glossers can be used to add extra shine to your lips. Their moisturizing qualities also help lips from becoming dry and parched.

15. If your mouth is too thin, wear a light shiny lipstick so that it looks thicker. A full mouth can be made to appear less so with a dark matte shade.

CHAPTER VI

THE "TOTAL" BEAUTY

The Romance of Fragrance: How to Choose and Use Fragrances to Create Your Own Personal Aura . . . Luxury Bath . . . Glossary of Fabergé Fragrance Terms . . . Manicures . . . Pedicures . . . Exercises . . . Do's and Don't's of Dieting

THE "TOTAL" BEAUTY

Fabergé has an extensive line of cosmetics for your face, your eyes, your mouth. Everything a woman needs to enhance her beauty can be found at the Fabergé counter of her favorite store. Stop by and see how much more beautiful you can be with the right makeup.

The Romance of Fragrance:
How to Choose and Use Fragrances to Create Your Own Personal Aura

Perfume can do a great deal to lift your spirits and reflect your personality. You can choose from a variety of different perfumes, and wear them according to your mood. That way when you're feeling cute and flirty you would choose one type of fragrance. When you are pensive and serious, you would want another. Whatever type fragrance you pick, your perfume will refresh you and delight both you and those

189

around you. In addition, it will add immeasurably to your femininity.

Fabergé has 7 different fragrances. Each one so different and unique it can suggest a whole personality of its own. Each one reflects a certain mood . . . a state of mind . . . a feeling.

When you're feeling light, carefree in a will-o'-the-wisp mood, you'll want *KiKU*. It has a hint of the chrysanthemum, a whisper of freshness and a feeling of candidness. It's perfect for walking hand-in-hand in the rain or anything else romantic. Faberge's *Xanadu* perfume, on the other hand, suggests an extremely exotic personality type. When you're feeling extra sexy, when your mood is sensual, pick Xanadu to flatter that mood. It's called the Sensuous Scent of the Seventies. Wear it when you're absolutely sure what you are up to.

Aphrodisia is a sophisticated scent. It's fragrance suggests a mood of chic, sleek polish. It's strictly for the woman who's calm sophisticated exterior covers a fire of personality.

Tigress is for those wild enough to wear it. Feline, uninhibited, direct. It's a fragrance that doesn't fool around.

Woodhue is a crisp, fresh, inquisitive type of perfume which says just that about its wearer. It's for your outdoorsy mood—so perfect for a picnic in the country.

Flambeau is different. You must be romantic, smoldering, flamboyant. If you're feeling shy, stay away from Flambeau. This perfume is for when you're feeling torchy.

And there's *Music*, the newest fragrance from Fabergé. It's young, colorful, honest and extremely down-to-earth. If you're willing to sing that song, then put on a little Music.

Whatever type fragrance you choose, for whatever mood you're in, here are some helpful hints on application:

Perfume should be worn at the pulse spots. Don't just dab it behind the ears and forget about it. Dab it behind the knees, on the palms, in the bends of the elbow, on the throat, along the hairline, and between the breasts. Always wear perfume so that it is not overpowering, keeping in mind that high humidity has a tendency to intensify the fragrance. Apply it with a light touch, as it is the strongest form of fragrance. Once the bottle is opened, use it generously, since it does not last indefinitely. Reapply about every four or five hours, keeping it in its own box, with the cap or stopper tightly in place. Never mix your fragrances. If you're wearing Xanadu, then match it with Xanadu spray cologne and Xanadu bath luxuries. In addition to using fragrance on your body, you can use it in your hair and on your lingerie for a total effect.

THE LUXURY BATH

To round out your fragrance wardrobe, be sure to use bath and body fragrances before and after your bath. Take your bath in a relaxing tubful of scented oil and splash on some soothing cologne and puff on a matching bath powder afterwards. Be sure to buy the bath oil that matches your perfume fragrance. Scented bath oils are used to moisturize your skin while bathing it in luxury. They have exceptionally long fragrance staying power. To add to the luxury of your bath, rest your head on a little neck-rest tub pillow. Just relax your head on the pillow, and set your hair or give yourself a manicure while in the tub.

Bathing can be your most relaxing time of day. You can melt away tensions, bad moods, even achiness while moisturizing your body. Your bath can be turned into a healthy, luxurious experience, easing away the cares of the day. Fabergé makes a whole line of bath products. There are rich moisturizing oils, soaps, light bubbling bath preparations and luxurious bath powders, body lotions and much more. Each is available in your favorite fragrance.

FABERGE'S GLOSSARY OF FRAGRANCE TERMS

Cologne/Toilet Water

Although cologne is traditionally a milder form of fragrance than toilet water, Faberge's cologne is of toilet-water strength and that is why Fabergé makes only one form of this lighter fragrance concentration.

Parfum Esprit Spray

This form of fragrance is exclusive to Fabergé. It is a touch more intensive than cologne and not quite as strong as perfume.

Splash-On

Traditionally a very mild form of fragrance, Fabergé makes splash-on in the same strength as cologne.

Perfume Oil for Body and Bath

This is an oil-based form of fragrance, and Fabergé makes a very pure perfume oil. It has the same intensity and lasting power of perfume.

Perfume

The strongest, most highly concentrated form of a particular fragrance in an alcohol base. Fabergé blends many essential oils to obtain the most intense fragrance, so it will last longer than ordinary perfumes.

MANICURES

Your hands deserve to be pampered . . . just like the rest of you. Therefore, make sure your beauty routine includes regular hand care. Use hand cream regularly. If your hands are extremely dry, here's a simple routine you can do before retiring to help them. Coat your hands with rich cream and cover with a pair of cotton gloves. Leave the gloves on for about forty-five minutes and remove. If your nails have a tendency to split, use a nail conditioner to strengthen them. Massage nails daily with cuticle massage cream. In addition, wear gloves when doing heavy housework.

Most important of all, treat yourself to weekly manicures. You can do a professional job by using

Faberge's Ceramic Glaze. It's a polish, base coat and sealer all in one. Fabergé is the only cosmetic company in the world that employs this exclusive nail formula. It's a scientific polish (in clear and frosted) that actually helps damaged nails and helps protect good nails from damage.

Fabergé has a whole line of nail products to assist you obtain the perfect manicure. Everything from cuticle remover to many marvelous new nail enamel colors. And don't forget Faberge's protective hand cream. The new formula now contains *aloe* which really helps hands become softer, smoother. And it's available in your favorite fragrance.

PEDICURES

While you're in the mood for pampering yourself, let's not forget about your feet. First soak your feet in some soapy suds for about fifteen minutes. This will soften up the calluses and remove flaky skin. Scrub your toes with a soft brush, paying special attention to the area between the toes. Dry toes with a soft towel and sprinkle them with powder. Push the cuticle straight back with an orangestick. Trim toenails straight across, being careful not to cut into the corners. Smooth the edges with an emery board. Separate each toe with a cotton ball. Apply two coats of nail polish.

If your feet are extremely dry, try Xanadu's Nitti-Gritti Pumice Lotion. It actually rubs away dry, rough, dead skin. Use it on all dry areas of your body . . . especially elbows. Xanadu's Salubria Lubricating Lotion is perfect to moisten, lubricate and soften those dry areas. In the evening, mix some in a little warm water, and soak your feet. In just one week's time, your feet will be softer and smoother.

If the nails on your toes have a tendency to split, break or peel, you will want to use Ceramic Glaze by Fabergé to help restore them to good condition.

EXERCISES

Dieting may reduce pounds, but exercise is necessary to reduce inches. In addition, if you have any problem areas, spot-reducing is a must. If you do these spot-reducing exercises properly, you will wind up with the measurements you want, and feeling just great.

Exercise should be included in your reducing program. Exercise, plus dieting, will give you the trim figure you are after in a shorter period of time. Once you reach your desired measurements, decide upon a permanent way of maintaining these measurements.

The first step in setting up an exercise program is taking your measurements. View yourself in front of a full-length mirror, taking down your proportions. Decide which areas need spot-reducing and find the right exercise to do the trick.

For midriff and stomach reducing, become more active in the sports world. Try tennis, swimming, volleyball, etc. Touching your toes with your fingertips is a good warmer-up. Do this about twenty-five times a day. In addition, you can lie down on the floor and do sit-ups. Clasp your hands behind your head while you lie on the floor. Inhale and exhale slowly as you sit up, touching your knee with your elbow. Repeat several times daily.

To reduce the thighs and hips, lie flat on the floor with your arms straight out. Lift one leg up, and swing it over the other leg to touch the floor. Keep your knees straight. Repeat the procedure, using the other leg. Give your neck a little exercise too by letting your head fall as far forward as possible, and lifting it back very slowly. Repeat about ten to fifteen times daily.

Besides dieting and exercise, you can look pounds thinner by improving your posture. Flatten your stomach by drawing your body up from the waist and straightening your shoulders out. This will give you a leaner, longer appearance.

There are many helpful books on the market which are quite inexpensive. It would be worth your while to purchase one and follow a regular routine of exercise.

Even if you are satisfied with your figure, you should follow a regular routine of exercise just to keep physically fit. You will feel better, too. A good set of exercises to follow just to keep in shape is in the *Royal Canadian Air Force Exercise Manual* available at most of your discount stores.

The Do's and Don't's of Dieting

Motivation is the keynote to successful dieting. You must really want to lose weight and you will. You can get this motivation by taking a good look at yourself in the mirror to get a close view at the battle of the bulge, or by pinning a picture of yourself in a bikini on the inside of the refrigerator to discourage frequent snacks.

The most important thing is to find a diet that works. There are all kinds of diets to choose from, including quick-weight-loss diets, grapefruit diets, steak and salad diets, etc. However, consult your doctor for the diet that's right for you. He can recommend a diet which not only makes you lose weight but keeps you nutritionally sound. Chances are, he will recommend a diet that cuts down on your caloric intake, while including all of the basic foods such as meat, fish, poultry, milk, bread, and cereals, etc.

However, here are some Do's and Don't's to get you started:

1. Do take a look at your supermarket shelves to pick up some of the low-calorie foods that help reduce pounds.

2. Don't go on a crash program for a short period of time and revert back to your old eating habits. Dieting is a way of life, and this means breaking old habits.

3. Do embark on a serious dieting plus exercising program. The combination of the two will insure quicker results.

4. Don't go on a quick-weight-loss diet for a long period of time. Quick-weight-loss diets give fast results, and although they are good morale boosters, shouldn't be continued for long periods.

5. Do concentrate on foods high in protein content. Eggs, fish, meat, cheese, milk, etc., build strong tissue, and burn up calories.

6. Don't indulge in alcoholic beverages while dieting. If you must drink, switch to dry wines or champagnes, and stay away from cocktails.

7. Do learn how to count calories. Carry a small calorie counter in your purse at all times.

8. Don't cut down on your water intake while dieting. Drinking water with your meals will cut down your appetite and therefore your caloric intake.

9. Do go to a good doctor before dieting. See which diet your doctor recommends and stick to it.

10. Don't eat fatty meats—lean meats only. Increase your intake of fish, and you will lose weight faster.

11. Do include more low-calorie foods in your diet. Drink skim milk and diet sodas, use margarine instead of butter, and try the artificial sweeteners instead of sugar to cut down on calories.

12. Don't lose patience about dieting. If you are not getting the results you want as fast as you want them —don't fret. Keep at it until you get the figure you've always wanted.

If you want to gain weight, just do the opposite of what your weight-reducing friends have to do. Increase your caloric intake, get plenty of rest, and eat, eat, eat. Be sure to include all the basic foods in your diet, plus more. Remember, if five meals a day, rather than three heavy meals, add up to more calories, then switch to the five-a-day program. In addition, if too many liquids at mealtime cut down your appetite, reduce your liquid intake.

If you set up a constant beauty routine for your hair, your complexion, and your body, you will find yourself looking more attractive, and feeling better, too.

INDEX